FOOLISH FIRE

GAY MEN'S PRESS

Foolish Fire

by Guy Willard

First published 1999 by Millivres Ltd,
part of the Millivres Prowler Group,
3 Broadbent Close, London N6 5GG

World Copyright © 1999 Guy Willard

A CIP catalogue record for this book is available
from the British Library

ISBN 1 902852 02 8

Distributed in Europe by Central Books,
99 Wallis Rd, London E9 5LN

Distributed in North America by InBook/LPC Group,
1436 West Randolph, Chicago, IL 60607

Distributed in Australia by Bulldog Books,
P O Box 300, Beaconsfield, NSW 2014

Printed and bound in the EU by WSOY, Juva, Finland

SIDE ONE

1. Pin-Ups

It all began for me on the very first day of PE class in junior high school. For the first time, the boys had been separated from the girls for a class, and we felt very grown-up about it. Sitting on the bleachers in the school gymnasium, we answered to our names as the boys' physical education teacher, Coach Kapp, called roll. He used only our last names.

"Sims!"

"Here!"

"Talbot!"

"Here!"

"Willard!"

"Here!" As usual, my name was the last one called.

Coach Kapp put away his roll book and began to give his orientation talk.

He was a short, well-built man with close-cropped hair and he wore a snug-fitting t-shirt and shorts. The tiny golden hairs on his legs were like honey-colored smoke floating softly over his tanned skin. His speech was crisp, curt, almost military. With the lights of the gym glinting off the lenses of his eyeglasses, and the whistle dangling from a string around his neck, he looked like a general barking out orders to his men.

Seeing that many of us had come without the things we'd need, he began by introducing all the gear we would have to purchase. To do this, he borrowed one of the boys' gym bags. As he dug out each item, he explained it: a gym shirt, gym shorts, sweat socks, tennis shoes, a towel, a washcloth, and something which caused a titter of nervous laughter to ripple among the boys when he held it up: an athletic supporter. A jock strap. Giggling with the others, I saw that, when worn, its cup fit snugly over the genitals, but the buttocks remained daringly exposed, framed diagonally by the elastic straps of the supporter.

The coach continued his talk by discussing general health practices, the need to eat nutritious foods and get plenty of sleep every night. He also stressed the importance of cleanliness and told us we would be expected to comply with certain guidelines in his class.

"Come on, I'll show you the locker room." His voice boomed and echoed high into the rafters of the gym.

He led us back around the bleachers and through a door at the far end of the basketball court.

The locker room turned out to be a dank, evil-smelling cement bunker. Kapp pointed out the lockers and the benches. "The showers are this way," he said.

We followed him around a projecting wall where a narrow passageway led to the shower room. When we'd all crowded into the small space, he gathered us around and said:

"The first thing you have to learn is to get over any shyness you might feel about undressing in front of others. Now we're all men here, so that shouldn't be any problem, right? There's nothing shameful about being seen in the buff by other guys." He said this in a sarcastic tone of voice as if explaining something very simple to small children. "It's something you're going to have to get used to anyway, so we may as well start right now."

We stirred uneasily.

"All right, I want everyone who's brought their gym gear today to take a shower."

There was a groan of protest at this but Kapp raised both hands in the air. "Come on, we haven't got much time."

So, with mixed feelings of discomfort and bravado, the boys who'd brought their gear began to comply. Those of us who hadn't brought our gear waited in amusement by the entry to the showers and eyed each naked boy as he came from the locker room. A few nervous jokes wavered in the air as some of the nude boys half-hugged themselves, or pretended to scratch or rub some part of their body in an attempt to hide as much skin as possible. Everyone felt self-conscious.

My mouth had gone dry at the prospect of having to undress in front of the others next time, but there was something else which usurped my attention as I watched the parade of naked boys. While most of their bodies were still childlike, baby-smooth and hairless, several of them, unknown to everyone else, had already matured.

I noted a very attractive boy named Doug whose shoulders were manfully broad. His body was burnished a deep bronze from lying on the beach all summer, and a pale strip of skin outlined the shape of phantom swim trunks about his hips. A thick, curly patch of pubic hair almost hid the penis which poked out like a saucy pink tongue. His balls were large and egg-shaped.

My eyes then went, of their own accord, to a boy named Ted. He was a quiet, likable boy who'd sat next to me in the fourth grade. Back then he'd been one of the smallest boys in class, but during the past summer he'd sprouted up like a bean-pole and his arms and legs looked gawkily long. Dangling down incongruously huge and out of proportion to the rest of his boyish frame were man-sized genitals from which the boys in class could barely keep their eyes... much to Ted's discomfort.

There were a few others whose bodies still looked chubby and soft with baby-fat, but who sported a soft, downy, shadow-like fuzz at their groins which was a promise of approaching maturity. The race for manhood had begun and these boys were leading the pack. I didn't have any pubic hair yet, and the sight of these developing bodies made me feel more than ever like a piping-voiced child.

"All right, into the showers, guys, all of you."

Coach Kapp herded all of us into the showers and explained how the hot and cold water worked. Then he led the clothed boys out toward the bleachers outside. Behind us steam had begun to roll out along the cement floor, and yells and cries could be heard above the hiss of water as horseplay commenced.

For the rest of the day I walked about school in a daze, numb with disbelief. I felt I was seeing double: whenever I looked at a classmate, I saw him not only in his clothes, but his naked body as I'd seen it in the showers that morning. It was as if I'd been endowed with super-vision, or was wearing those X-ray spectacles advertised so often in the back pages of comic books.

* * *

That Saturday, Jack and I went out to the old swimming hole across the tracks, out toward the airport. Though it was September, the weather was still warm enough for a swim.

Jack was my best friend. We'd grown up together, and he'd always been the leader in our childhood games. Maybe it was because he was so big for his age, but he somehow seemed much older and more mature than me, though we were the same age.

For one thing, his voice was already a burry tenor, his tiny adam's apple bobbing up and down whenever he talked. The voices of our classmates represented every pitch from a sweet boy soprano to a deep manly growl. Some boys were caught between changes, their voices sounding a little hoarse, as if they'd caught a cold. Their in-between status was treacherously betrayed by sudden jolting soprano yelps which caused everyone to jump in surprise and laugh afterwards at the red-faced boy.

The swimming hole, as we called it, was actually an old abandoned reservoir created by damming a stream that ran through the scrubland west of town. A sign posted there declared it off-limits, but all the kids used it when the warm weather came. On one shore was a group of huge boulders which came down to the very edge of the water. One rock jutted out over the water, its flat projection forming a smooth ledge. This was our diving platform.

Jack had worn his usual cut-off shorts instead of swim trunks. I watched the white strings from their frayed edges play about his thighs as he stretched his arms up to peel off his t-shirt. He tossed down his t-shirt and looked at me.

"Come on, Guy, what are you waiting for?"

Standing up on the flat ledge, I began stripping off my clothes. I had worn my bathing trunks under them. I rolled my jeans and t-shirt into a bundle and stuffed them into the shade.

Suddenly Jack grabbed me by the wrists and pushed me to the edge of the rock.

"What are you doing, Jack?"

He shoved me over the edge and I went down into the water, yelling and kicking my legs. As soon as I was in the water, he plunged in right after me with a loud splash, surfacing almost immediately to let out a long, exhilarated whoop.

We swam lazily about, splashing water onto each other, dunking each other's heads. I would dive down, then come up, pulling at his legs from under water. Our cries were lost in the vast, cloudless sky. When we got tired of playing, we pulled ourselves up, dripping, onto the ledge. The sun had baked it and it burned our feet.

Gingerly, we limped pigeon-toed toward our towels, shivering, hugging ourselves, our bodies slick and wet, our hair dripping. As we dried ourselves off, Jack flicked his wet hair at me, then rolled his towel under his arm. With my help, he sought toeholds on the rock behind us, scrambling up its steep side. From its flat top he called down for his sun-tan lotion, which I tossed up to him. I saw him begin to unroll his towel.

Left to myself, I sat in the shade dangling my legs over the side, gazing out over the flat landscape. The gully through which the stream ran could barely be seen as a slight crease in the terrain. Not a cloud marred the expanse of sky.

The faint smell of my own sweat made me conscious of a little breeze.

"I think I'll take a walk around," I called up to Jack. "Wanna come?"

"Nah. You go ahead."

I picked up my shoes, leaned over the edge away from the water and felt them drop away from my hands like live birds. Two distant-sounding plops echoed up, seemingly unrelated to the shoes hitting the ground. I began climbing down the far corner of the ledge. It was much easier to gain toeholds on the rock with my bare feet.

"Hey!" I called up from the ground.

No answer.

I put on my shoes and began walking around. Just beyond the group of boulders beside the reservoir was a low wooded hill which overlooked the whole scene. I made my way up a steep embankment and entered the shade of the trees.

It was cool in here; I kicked my way through the undergrowth, slicing through the dappled shade, feeling the slap of twigs and low branches against my bare chest. I stopped to examine a colony of grotesquely enlarged toadstools nestled near the foot of a vine-smothered tree. The sound of crying insects was almost deafening. I felt a trickle of sweat creep down my back, then another. I wiped my brow and shivered at the woods' coolness.

The grass rustled nearby. I turned my head quickly but saw nothing. The weeds shook again. Perhaps it was a small animal. I pushed ahead, carefully thrusting aside low branches and vines. A rank, fungoid odor hung in the cool, close air. Above me, beyond the interlacing web of branches, was the sky, pure and blue like the hint of a distant ocean.

I stopped.

I'd reached the huge spreading oak which crowned the top of the hill. With its gnarly bark and the myriad woody vines embedded in its surface, it reminded me of an illustration I'd seen in a book of ancient fairy tales.

I found a handhold and easily climbed up the length of the main trunk, then swung higher and higher into the swaying branches, glimpsing vaster prospects as the surrounding countryside opened up to my eyes. We were far enough away from the city for me to imagine that we were all alone on a desert island.

I stopped to catch my breath. My chest was red from rubbing against the bark, tiny bits of which clung to my damp skin. I wiped my brow again and glanced downward.

I was virtually suspended over the boulders far below. If I lost my grip I knew I would plunge down to my death... I tightened my hold on the branch. For a moment my head swam and I had to shut my eyes.

When I opened them again I saw, like a vision so close it seemed I could just reach out and touch him, Jack lying upon his beach towel sunbathing. He was flat upon his stomach so that the sun could bronze his shoulders and back. His head was turned aside, pillowed upon his hands, and his eyes were closed. He was completely unaware of my presence just above him, hidden in the dense foliage.

I gazed at his strong, broad shoulders... at the smooth back which rose and fell evenly with his breathing. Just as I'd suspected, he was much better built than any of the boys in my PE class. He had the body of a boy much older than us, the body of a grown man.

Suddenly he was twisting around, turning his head so he could look straight up at me. Thinking I'd been heard, I made ready with a jest or yell to cover up for my long silent contemplation. My muscles tensed up... But apparently he'd only turned onto his back so that his front side could be exposed to the sun. I was still safe.

I continued to watch as he brought his arms up and crossed his hands over his face to shield his eyes from the sun's glare. That was when I saw, nestled snugly within each armpit, a dark patch of curly hairs. It was like coming across a cache of hidden treasure. I had never suspected their presence, and this sudden revelation transformed my childhood friend into a strange, exalted being. He now looked like a young god reclining on a mountainside.

I felt dizzy. I knew that if I were spotted now in my secret perch, I'd have no excuse for remaining silent for so long. And the slightest movement on my part was bound to be noticed now that he was facing upward. I had no choice but to remain as I was. Feeling wretched, I continued to gaze down at the smooth stomach which undulated with his shallow breathing, making the dark concavity of his navel shiver and dance.

I prayed for a diversion, some noise that would distract his attention long enough for me to slip away. The urge to escape was overpowering...

My arms were growing tired from hanging on; the muscles in my right thigh were beginning to cramp. I cursed myself for coming up here in the first place, and then for not letting him know where I was. An edge of panic crept into my mind, agitating my breathing. And still I continued to gaze down at the boy whose body I was seeing for the first time as though it were a complete stranger's...

The sound of crying insects drummed into my ears... became a wailing... became a screeching.

* * *

Like most of my friends, I kept a secret collection of girly magazines hidden in my closet. I don't know why I started it— probably only because all the others did. We would look at these magazines together after school, and trade them off when we got tired of them.

The truth was that I felt a little silly whenever I looked at pictures of nude women. I couldn't understand the smirking interest boys showed in them—it was all so childish. I never got as excited as they did.

The flawless, perfect women in the magazines looked so airbrushed and plastic, with their pure white teeth and every hair in place. Their breasts tended to be oversized to unsightly proportions, while below, their tiny smudges of pubic hair always gave me the feeling of something missing. For me, a woman's body represented only the idea of 'otherness'. Nothing could be more different from how I and my friends looked naked. I secretly suspected that it was this 'otherness' alone which excited the boys so much.

I really had to keep from laughing every time I looked at a certain centerfold pin-up—the favorite one, by consensus, among my friends. She was blonde-haired, blue-eyed, and baby-faced. And her breasts were enormous; it was upon them that all my friends were fixated. They loved breasts, the bigger the better, and this simple-minded equation summed up the imbecilic geometry of their desire.

This woman's breasts looked simply cartoon-like, so ridiculously huge that her slender torso below them seemed barely able to support such a heavy mass. The nipples on them stared out like a pair of pink idiot eyes.

In contrast with the rest of her tanned body, the breasts were pale, their whiteness making them look as if they were balloons being blown up—the color of the balloons fading as they stretched and stretched, growing bigger and bigger, threatening to pop at any second.

To me it seemed as if the desirability of women and girls was inflamed by the furtiveness of the boys' talk, as though the talk itself were the aphrodisiac. Maybe the idea of doing something illicit was what gave them their biggest thrill. But all their talk couldn't hide the emptiness which lay behind it all.

Perhaps my jaded attitude stemmed from the fact that pictures of nude women were nothing new to me: I'd been sneaking peeks at my mother's art books ever since I was ten.

On the top row of the bookcase in the living room was a set of books my mother had bought when she was in college. She had majored in art, and most of the books were collections of the work of her favorite artists: Gauguin, Renoir, and Cezanne. Paintings of nude women were quite common in them. But one day as I was browsing through her collection, I discovered something a little more intriguing.

It was a volume called *The French Neo-Classicists and Romantics*, containing works by David, Ingres, Delacroix, and Fragonard, whose names meant nothing to me. When I opened it up at random however, I discovered a fabulous world of lush tints and dynamic action. The color plates were unbelievably detailed, and glowing with a vibrant life. Many of the paintings had themes from Greek mythology, with gods and goddesses completely nude, or with their genitals just barely covered by a stray piece of cloth.

It was the men who rivetted my attention. The color of a man's flesh—so much darker and more alive than a woman's—seemed to set off something inside me I'd never before experienced. As I gazed at pictures of scantily clad or nude men frozen in action poses with their glowing, sinewy torsos bursting with life, I felt my interest was somehow sinful. I dreaded being caught looking at these pictures. Yet, strangely enough, this dread actually increased the pleasure I got.

One picture showed several men bathing in a river or lake, their genitals unblushingly exposed. I couldn't believe that such things could be shown so openly. The mixture of shame and pleasure I felt gave me such a unique, oddly visceral thrill that I went

16

through all the books in my mother's collection to seek out similar pictures.

In time I became more familiar with the world of classical art and sculpture. My interest had turned into a craving, a hunger, almost. I sought out more and more art books to satisfy it, knowing somehow that my obsession would be considered unhealthy by others. Yet I didn't care. In fact, I suspected that if it hadn't been for the forbidden nature of it, I might not have spent so much time in my pursuit. I might not have done it at all.

Before the art books, it had been comic books.

The comic books I'd loved as a boy had always been filled with brawny, muscular super-heroes. Comic book artists always seemed to endow their men with an exaggerated musculature never to be found in real life. My daydreams were centered on certain visions inspired by them: Tarzan of the apes, almost naked, swinging through the jungle on a fat vine; westerns, with their bare-chested Indian warriors; Roman epics, swarming with brawny Christian slaves. And on the back pages of these comic books I was treated to advertisements for muscle-building courses, featuring grainy black and white photographs of well-built men wearing skimpy briefs, flexing their biceps and chests, or exercising with artificial flexors.

These muscle men could be seen in the movies, too, and on television. I was switching channels idly one night when I came across a late-night movie being shown, a historical epic of some kind, taking place sometime during the period of the Roman Empire.

A recalcitrant Christian slave was being punished by a Roman warrior. The slave was stripped of everything but a tiny loincloth made of animal hide and led to a raised dais between two huge pillars. There, each of his wrists was secured with thongs to the pillars so that he stood with his arms stretched out to either side.

Under the hot sun, his bulging muscles glistened with sweat. He gritted his teeth stoically as the sadistic Roman soldier began flogging him repeatedly with a small, many-thonged whip. At first the slave tried to show his contempt for his tormentor by making light of the punishment. But eventually it got to be too much for him; he was thrashing about in obvious pain. Finally he couldn't take it anymore and lost consciousness, his head dropping to his chest. The background music became saccharinely lush at this point, the pure, celestial harmonies of an angelic choir swelling to a heart-melting climax.

My feelings as I watched this scene were strangely mixed. I felt sympathy and pity for the slave, of course. He was so handsome, and his suffering gave him an almost saintly appearance. But the brutal Roman soldier—with his expression of obvious delight in his sport—caused another, more earthy thrill to grip my body.

It was difficult getting to sleep that night. In my mind I kept reliving the anguish of the tortured slave. I thought of his contorted face, the writhings of his attractive body, and of his tormentor's cruel look. The staccato crack of the whip as it lashed against the sweating back, chest, and thighs still rang in my ears. The beads of blood flicked onto the sand...

I imagined my own wrists being tightly bound, my arms stretched out to both sides, secured to fat pillars. I was wearing nothing but my undershorts... no, my briefs were brutally yanked down and I was completely naked. I closed my eyes and imagined I heard a sharp crack! And then another—crack!... another... crack! And when I opened my eyes again in the darkness, I could almost feel the stinging welts raised on my back and shoulders, the trickle of warm blood licking down my arms, the keen bite of leather thongs around my wrists.

*　*　*

I was visiting a friend's house one day when I discovered something lying underneath the backyard hammock, discarded by his older brother.

It was a muscle magazine, the first I'd ever seen.

Flipping through it, I became intrigued by the many photos of well-muscled, bikini-clad men. I knew it was ostensibly a health magazine devoted to physical fitness and body-building, but it was obvious to me that all the models had been chosen for their physical beauty.

As much as I craved to possess this magazine, I knew I couldn't let my friend know it, for he was sure to find an excuse for not letting me have it, just to irk me. So I deliberately put on a casual air as I riffled its pages in a bored manner and tossed it aside.

He pounced upon it and, finding a picture, imitated the man's pose in an exaggerated fashion, flexing imaginary muscles.

I obligingly laughed at his pantomime and was secretly grateful when he tossed the magazine away under some bushes. Later, on my way home, I swerved my bicycle around to his backyard to retrieve the magazine, slipping it under my shirt as I pedalled away, my heart hammering with excitement.

In order to examine it in uninterrupted leisure, I locked myself in the bathroom as soon as I got home. Indeed, the tight feeling of excitement in the pit of my stomach made defecation seem imminent. Sitting on the toilet seat with my pants down around my ankles, I began slowly flipping through the pages, eyeing pictures of handsome men with bulging biceps and massive chests, their muscles etched in well-defined contours.

With the sea as a background, they flexed and posed in various attitudes, surrounded by groups of admiring girls who touched and stroked their hard muscles. The camera had caught them at angles best designed to show off their bodies. They were like statues of Greek gods, smooth-skinned and hairless, gleaming as if made of polished steel. I felt my breath come short. Page after page was filled with these fabulous heroes, so magnificently endowed that a young boy like me could only pine with envy.

It was only after some time had passed that I noticed for the first time the reason for the stiff, nudging prod I'd felt against my belly. Dropping the magazine, I stared down at the biggest penis I'd ever seen in my life. I couldn't even recognize it as my own. Grotesquely changed, it was poking straight up against my stomach, pressing so hard that it hurt, its skin stretched so tight that it shone like a plump sausage. Fat, ropy blue veins throbbed on its exposed underside, and a brown seam bisected its swollen length.

It didn't belong to me. A stranger had inexplicably usurped the place of a familiar friend.

2. Physical Education

In the winter, Coach Kapp introduced us to freestyle wrestling. The entire gym floor was covered with mats, and the basketball court looked strangely transformed, as if it had received a blanket of snow overnight.

From the very start I became enthusiastic about wrestling. My father had been a champion wrestler in high school and would have received a scholarship to go to college if he hadn't broken a collar bone in a motorcycle accident. He taught me all the holds and moves. I enjoyed the rough contact of the sport which gave me a chance to delight in my own speed and agility. To my amazement, I found that I was one of the stronger boys in class.

I loved the thrill of pinning a weaker opponent to the mat, feeling the gradually feebler struggle beneath me, the labored breathing against my neck and ear—and hearing the coach's handslap against the mat indicating a victorious pin.

PE became my favorite class period. Maybe it was because of its special ambience of masculine camaraderie... the shouted encouragement of the boys when I wrestled, the coach's sharp whistle echoing through the gym's rafters.

My strongest opponent was Ted. Though we were in the same weight class, he was taller than me by a good six inches. Indeed, he seemed to grow taller by the day, but the added height only made him seem frailer. He was always making some reference to his own height as though demeaning my lagging growth, and this was a source of irritation for me. I'd wrestled him once and beaten him, but recently he was making a good showing against the others in our group.

Coach Kapp had scheduled a tournament to determine the best wrestlers in each weight class. On the last day before the tournament, we were free to practice with the partner of our choice. Naturally, I picked Ted. A group of boys formed a ring around us on the mats, eager to see the outcome. One of them acted as the referee.

Raising our arms like attacking bears we lunged at each other, grappling in the standing position. I pressed my head against his shoulder while he bent down a little to lock his head alongside mine.

He was so thin I thought he'd fold at the slightest attack. I made a grab for his leg but to my surprise he easily stepped out of reach. Then he reached an arm down to snag my leg, and his arms were so long that he had no trouble pulling me off balance and tripping me down to the mat.

As I crashed down I was momentarily stunned, but quickly scrambled up and maneuvered around to grip him in a half-nelson. With a surprising knowledge of tactics, he rolled away, pulling me around onto my back. Then he rolled over on top of me, completely covering me.

I squeezed my legs around his thigh in order to get some leverage or a pivot with which to flip him over. But when I felt my shoulders being forced down I began bucking and thrashing, arching my back as the coach had demonstrated in order to escape a pin. It was to no avail. Beneath me I could feel the damp closeness of the mat, and above me, the burning rub of his salty-tasting skin. Ruthlessly and relentlessly he bore down with all his weight until my shoulders touched.

A slap on the mat. He'd pinned me.

"One more time," I panted, getting to my feet. My face felt flushed not only from the exertion but from the humiliation of being beaten. "I wasn't ready yet," I said.

We grappled again. This time, when I felt his hands grope for my thigh I was prepared. But as I stepped back out of his reach I lost my balance. I'd gone too far back and he took advantage of it by pulling me forward.

Luckily I had enough presence of mind to land on my stomach, the safest position after a take-down. I felt him drop onto my back without hesitation, then snatch my right arm up from under my stomach and pull it up behind my back. Again I was put into a vulnerable position.

My amazement at his skill was outweighed only by my own humiliating lack of it. I could feel the full length of his body on me but could do nothing, though I tried to twist my hips out from under the hold. I was pressed too tightly to the mat.

"Give up?" his strained voice breathed in my ear.

"Never!" The stuffy smell of the old wrestling mats, pungent from years of usage and the sweat of generations of boys, only seemed to augment my despair. I twisted wildly and managed to free the lower half of my body. In doing so I heard a loud smack as

I accidentally knocked my head against his jaw. His body went slack. "Sorry! Are you all right?"

"Yeah." He touched his tongue tenderly. "I'm okay. Let's wrestle."

We got back up to a standing grapple. This time I dropped down to the mat and, hooking my arms around his knees, shoved him off balance. He went down with a yell and while he was sprawled flat I scurried around to get him into a pinning hold.

Quickly I slid my left hand down between his thighs and fumbled for a body lock before he could recover. I knew I had a victory now. No one had ever escaped from this hold.

As he became aware of the imminent pin he began rocking frantically in an effort to loosen my grip. But I was fired by the taste of coming victory and only tightened my clutch.

"Give up?"

"No!"

He only increased his resistance. I'd never thought he had such a will to win. My own strength was giving out and I wondered if I could maintain my advantage long enough to pin him. I reached for another surge of strength.

As he frantically sought an escape, it dawned on me with a mild surprise what was rubbing and pressing so intimately against the inside of my elbow. At the recognition I instantly froze, wondering whether my fumbling might have hurt him. But that was just the opening he needed. He twisted me over and bulldozed me onto my back.

"Hey!"

Now he was once again sprawled full-length atop me, and I was faced with the prospect of another defeat.

"That wasn't fair!"

Both my hands were pinned up by my shoulders, held flat by the weight of his hands. His upper body was pressing down against my shoulders and chest. I cursed my momentary lapse which had so suddenly turned the tide against me. I knew I was pinned but stubbornly refused to accept it. A rage welled up inside me, half at my own stupidity, and half at Ted's hitherto unsuspected strength.

"You're pinned," I heard his muffled voice say somewhere above and behind my ear. I felt the hot press of his neck against my cheek.

"Not yet!"

I struggled feebly but it only brought on another burst of vigor. His body writhed down harder to ensure a pin. I wrapped my legs around his thighs in an effort to get my ankles around into a leg lock. He felt the maneuver and began madly wriggling from side to side to shake it off. I felt his hardness rubbing down along the inside of my thigh. I wondered if he knew I could feel it.

"Give up?"

"No!"

I realized that I, too, was hard and he might be able to feel me against his stomach. He was panting loudly, and the exertion had made his skin flush hot.

I felt a strange new sensation come over me. I began to panic.

"Get off!" I yelled, squirming.

He made no move.

"I said get off!" I screamed.

At this new, desperate tone of voice he rolled off me with a worried look. I scrambled up to my feet and rushed to the restroom behind the bleachers. Entering the nearest stall, I slammed the door shut behind me and tugged my shorts roughly down, then man-handled my jock strap halfway down my thighs.

Something was coming and I was scared. Whatever it was, I didn't want it to happen in my clothes. I knew it was impossible to urinate the way I was, but something insisted on coming out and it felt terribly uncomfortable. An incredible sense of urgency came over me. I wanted it to end—I urged it with my hand.

Something happened.

Something happened and it felt strange. I stared down at the pale milk-colored liquid which had oozed out like watery tears and knew that whatever it was was over, though I couldn't say how I knew. At the same time, I felt the strangest sense of relief. It was the most mystifying thing that had ever happened to me, and I was scared.

Only after some time had passed did I realize that Ted was outside the door softly knocking and inquiring in a worried tone of voice if anything was wrong.

"I'm okay."

Quickly I wiped away the milk and pulled my shorts back up. I felt shaken, afraid of facing him.

"I'm sorry, Guy," he said. "I didn't mean to be so rough. I guess I got a little carried away. You're not mad at me, are you?"

"No." I felt too ashamed to go out after what had just happened.

"Come on out, then."

I knew if I didn't go out he might think there really was something wrong with me. Shakily, I opened the door and, not daring to look at him, walked straight past him out to the mats, away from the others, where I sat down cross-legged. I wondered if he could guess what had happened, whether my shame was written all over my face.

He squatted down beside me. "No harm done, right? We're still friends?"

I wanted to be left alone with the mixed-up feelings inside me and felt irritated at his hovering about with such naive stupid concern. Yet I managed to shake off my sulk and clasp his extended hand. We shook hands solemnly, adultly.

* * *

Something new had come into my life. I had found a brand new toy. Gradually, fumblingly, I began to discover its delightful uses—this toy I'd had all along, not knowing its secret powers. In no time at all it dominated my life. At least once a day I felt compelled to respond to its irresistible call.

The first few times I did it I felt crushed with shame immediately afterwards. I thought everyone would know what I'd done... that it was transparently evident in my guilty features. But after I survived a week, then two weeks without being detected, I began to get braver. In fact I loved the brazen, defiant nature of the act. Its implicit rebellion thrilled me. I almost dared them to catch me at it.

At first I thought I was all alone with my secret, the only one in the whole world to have discovered it. But gradually I became aware that other boys knew of it... quite a few other boys, more than I would have guessed. And in a way this cheapened my secret.

I learned that it even had a dictionary name—masturbation—though the boys endowed it with numerous pet names—'beating off', 'jacking off', 'whacking off', etc. And I guessed from the sneaky smirks they exchanged whenever the topic came up that almost all of them did it, though most tried to deny it or even claimed a complete ignorance of it.

Yet the very fact that they knew of its existence—and more, tried to hide the fact—branded them, too, as conspirators in the secret brotherhood. And that added further fuel to my fantasies, for now I could pick out any boy in class and picture him stroking himself.

I began to pay covert attention to other boys' penises. Hitherto, when I'd found myself beside another boy at a urinal I'd averted my eyes from shame. Now I glanced surreptitiously downward, knowing I was safe from detection. I carefully noted the size and shape of his penis, the furtive way he tried to cover it with his hand, the jiggly shake afterwards when he was done.

My schooldays were now a daydreamy haze. From early morning, as soon as I got up, I looked forward to the day's masturbation, planning when, where, and how I would accomplish it.

In class my stomach was knotted up all day at the thought of it. I couldn't concentrate on the teacher's words or my studies, and my grades began to drop. The mere thought of masturbating was arousing, and the almost constantly erect state of my penis was an incessant call for attention. I couldn't say anymore whether I masturbated in response to my body's arousal, or whether my obsessive thinking about the act aroused me.

I constantly sought new ways of increasing or prolonging my pleasure, for though it was so intense, it was over so quickly. The actual climax was an instantaneous moment in time, gone almost before I could savor it, with my mind in a hazy swoon. Sometimes the entire process from excited unzipping to panicky clean-up took very much less than a minute—even as little as twenty or thirty seconds.

It was the dreaming of it which took up all the time... so that when it was over I often felt a tremendous sense of let-down and disappointment. If only the sweet moment could last and last... if only the eye-blink could be turned into a steady, heart-stopping gaze.

I tried everything, hoping I would stumble upon an undiscovered variation which would give me the ultimate pleasure.

I did it in the shower at home where I languorously soaped myself until I was all covered with suds, stroking myself with the now-familiar rhythm I'd instinctively discovered to be the one which gave the greatest pleasure, enchanted by the slick lubrication. And in the thundering spray I could moan as loudly as I wished. Or I could do it in the bathtub where I would watch, fascinated, the emergence under water of a billowing, ribbon-like white streamer.

Locking myself in the toilet, I pictured the boys I'd seen naked in PE class that day, concentrating my mind on this boy or that—Ted, Tony, or Doug—and keeping my eyes closed until the penultimate instant when I opened them to watch with an almost detached amazement the incredible white leap land on the tiled floor many feet away.

Sometimes I used pillows. Lying naked upon my bed, I would slip a pillow under me to cushion my pelvis. Then, pretending to be rubbing against the hard muscles of a fellow wrestler, I moved my hips to the rhythm which my hand had learned. And I hugged another pillow tightly to my chest as if I were clasping the struggling boy. I became so wrought up that I had to roll to the side of the bed so I wouldn't wet the pillowcase, cupping a hand to feel the warm catch moisten my palm. Later I spread tissue paper on the lower pillow so I could continue my fantasy wrestling without fear of leaving a trace (for by now, the ejaculate was a thick white paste.)

I tried out all the rooms of the house as if each new place were a variation of the same act, a new and different spicing... in my parents' bedroom, in my sister's room, in the living room, in my father's den with its musty smell of old books and the rubbery smell of scuba diving equipment. I did it in the kitchen sink, running the tap to wash away the evidence. I did it in the garage where I could hear people passing by just outside. One time I did it in a neighbor's house when I had to use their bathroom.

On the school bus I furtively stroked myself with my hand in my pocket while girls chatted just a seat away... and in class under my desk while the teacher wrote upon the blackboard, stopping just short of too late. (And how I wished I could go all the way without ejaculating!) I did it in the boys' room where the privacy of a stall offered me a mad moment of delight snatched in the middle of the school day, often with boys just outside.

I did it the first thing in the morning as soon as I was up—for I almost always woke to a stiff erection. I did it at night among the bushes in my backyard where no one could spot me. I did it right in the hallway of my home in broad daylight during the two or three minutes in which my mom used the toilet. The element of danger, the risk of getting caught gave the act a special sense of urgency.

Normally one session was enough to leave me feeling sated for a while—or rather, free me from the tension of thinking about it all the time, giving me a temporary respite from my addiction. However, I sometimes felt like testing my endurance by doing it three, four, five times a day, pushing myself to my limits. One Saturday when I had the house to myself, I managed, by spacing them out, a record-breaking eight times—until I was 'shooting blanks', coming without any discharge—pushed on by a dogged determination to dredge to the roots of my obsession and be freed of it once and for all.

Sometimes I felt guilty about doing it so often. I thought of the whispered warnings about what happened when a boy did it too much and would go through a period of repentance when I vowed to quit once and for all. It never lasted long, however. At night I tossed and turned, unable to sleep. When I did manage to drop off, it was a restless slumber broken by intermittent wakefulness. And as the night progressed, I found myself pulling off my pajamas, then my underwear, until I was completely nude beneath the sheets, feverish with unsatisfied longing.

These attempts at chastity always ended up with a guilty half-hearted fondling which very quickly modulated into a furious pumping. I discovered to my amazement that these periods of abstention only served to increase my eventual pleasure. The climax was positively gut-wrenching, leaving me so shattered that I was momentarily unable or unwilling to even lift a hand to clean off my befouled face.

And so I sometimes purposely imposed these periods of celibacy to heighten my enjoyment of an increasingly routine act.

* * *

For the boys in seventh grade, body hair was still the definitive sign of physical maturity, and those of us who didn't even have pubic hair yet would cover our genitals in shame every time we took our showers in PE.

I felt more and more depressed each time I spotted another boy in the locker room sporting a shy new smudge of down-like pubic hair. In the steamy haze of the showers these boys were like newly-hatched chicks showing off their first badges of manhood, proud of their fledgling adult status. By the spring term of seventh grade, fully half of the boys had 'arrived'. I lived with the fear that I would never join them; the sight of my own smooth, baby-bare pubis was a constant source of humiliation.

Every morning after tumbling out of bed, the first thing I did was examine myself, running a hopeful finger over my pubis. Always there was nothing—only bare skin... detestable girl-smooth skin.

Finally, one morning I received my first sign of hope. I was still half asleep in bed when I caught myself rubbing a vague itch. When I realized what I was doing, I sat bolt upright. 'It's coming,' I thought. Throwing off my covers, I pulled my pajama bottoms down. In the early morning light nothing looked changed, yet I could somehow sense that it was arriving at last, the pubic hair for which I'd practically given up hope.

Every morning after that I tenderly caressed with my fingertips the harvest of downy fuzz which grew there, imagining I could see it getting thicker by the day. Then one morning, to my elation, I definitely spotted minuscule shoots of hair like scattered blades of grass shyly breaking the soil.

Day by day—almost before my very eyes, it seemed—the hairs grew thicker, spreading out their fine spider-web filigrees of soft brown through which the skin could still be glimpsed. No longer would I have to hold my bath towel shyly in front of me as I crept toward the showers. I could now drape it boldly around my neck as I strolled around the locker room. And I could take my time in the showers from now on, soaping myself as unselfconsciously as the others did.

With the first sign of maturity upon me I felt as if I had been vouchsafed a promise of all the others still to come, the rest of my masculine birthright: greater height, a voice change, underarm hair, a beard. Yes, there were two or three boys in class who already shaved. How I envied them, with a yearning virtually indistinguishable from worship. I always felt a thrill of delight each time these boys, in the showers, raised an arm to scrub their backs, brazenly exposing a lovely underarm bush beaded with tiny, shivering, transparent drops of water.

The musty smell these boys left on their clothes, that briny aroma which lingered on their t-shirts in PE class, was an exotic perfume for me. I often lowered my nose toward my own armpit trying to evoke it. Sometimes when I was clowning around with a friend I would sniff his underarm like an animal and pretend to be offended by the odor, fanning the air in front of my face and holding my nose. But the truth was—and I never dared admit it to anyone—I found that masculine smell very arousing.

* * *

It was Saturday afternoon and there was no one home. My parents had gone to see a movie with my sister so I knew I had the house all to myself for the next three hours. It was raining outside and I couldn't play baseball with my friends. But I had no desire to leave the house.

I made sure the front door was locked, then made my way to my parents' room. The full-length mirror on the inside of the closet door was like a portal opening into a whole new world of pleasures...

I stood before the mirror just looking at myself for a while. Then gradually I let my mind go blank in order to slip more easily into my fantasy. Narrowing my eyes to create a hazy effect with my lashes, I imagined that my reflection was another boy, a complete stranger, upon whom I was spying, and who was ignorant of my presence.

Keeping an oblique image of him in view, I slowly began to undress, watching him go through the same motions. I saw him peel out of his shirt and unbuckle his belt, letting his pants slide down to his ankles. There he stood, clad in nothing but his cotton briefs, with an uncertain look upon his face, a loose pile of clothes scattered about his feet.

We regarded each other with looks of mutual admiration mingled with an irresistible coyness... selfconsciously running our fingers through our hair, trying to act nonchalant. At some point he'd begun caressing his own chest and shoulders, then gently kneading his buttocks over his briefs.

Finally—after some time had passed... time enough to create an unbearable tension of expectancy and longing—we both stooped slightly and, in one motion, shyly stepped out of our briefs. As this last barrier was removed, I caught my breath at the sight offered so wantonly to my eyes. Though he tried clumsily to hide it, I could see the erection blossoming behind his concealing fingers.

Without looking at his face for fear of breaking the mood, I continued to gaze in admiration at his body. And as if he were consciously gratifying this desire, he turned his body this way and that, proudly showing it off, allowing me to view it from every possible angle: the thrilling side view of the steep-angled erection; the front view which displayed the clean taper from chest to waist, the smooth belly, the wispy bush from which protruded the en-gorged shaft; and the back view (for which I had to use a small, hand-held mirror) which showed the tight roundness of both buttocks and the enticing cleft where they met.

After this silent pantomime we gradually approached each other, shyly reaching out our hands... and touched fingertips. I ran my finger across the reflection, then brought my body closer until my erection was touching his, tip to tip, then pressed flat. The cool smooth barrier prevented me from moving my whole body into his—I wished I could merge completely with him.

Looking up suddenly I saw his face from up close—so close I couldn't recognize his features. I brought my lips to his in a cool smooth kiss... a kiss which could never touch. I squirmed against him, frustrated by the limits of reality... and broke the delicate web of fantasy. The mirror was just too smooth and cool and flat.

I backed the lower half of my body away and saw that the other boy, too, could no longer restrain himself. He had gripped himself, and his balled fist was a furious blur. I concentrated upon his face and watched it go through all the usual stages: first, an intent, serious look, the pink tip of his tongue visible between biting teeth; then the stupid slack look as the tides of pleasure rose, the eyelids growing heavy; then the silly smile as the rapid approach was glimpsed, the sap rising till a trickle leaked from the brimming tip; and then the teeth bared like a growling dog's, the neck muscles corded in tension, the nose wrinkled, the entire face contorted as if wracked by acute pain; and finally a momentary blankness as my whole body was jolted by spasms of the purest, most delicious pleasure... spinning rainbows out into black, black space; and immediately after, the face visible again, looking pale and drawn, ashen and wasted.

My heart pounding violently, I dully watched as several fat gobs of pearly spit slowly crawled down the surface of the mirror. Inside my mind, the thunderclap's echo was rolling away, dying, but my body was still tingling and shivering from its violent galvanization.

The boy in the mirror, guilt stamped on every feature, rushed into his clothes with an urgency that bordered on panic.

3. How I Spent My Summer Vacation

I was up in the Fort with my cousin Bobby. The Fort was a treehouse in my backyard I'd built with the help of my dad. Actually, my dad had started out by helping me build it, but growing impatient with my incompetence, had taken over the job himself, grimly, expertly hammering the boards into place, stepping back to survey his handiwork while I stood off to one side watching it get built. I'd never been mechanically minded, nor handy with tools, and I only felt in his way whenever we worked together on something.

Ever since it got built, the Fort was the place I liked to escape to, especially in the summer. I even slept in it sometimes, feeling like a boy drifting on a raft downstream. Naturally, whenever Bobby came for a visit, we would come up here as much as possible.

Every June, at the start of summer vacation, it was a custom for his family to visit us for about a week before proceeding on to the coast. His mother and mine were very close as sisters, and our fathers had gone to the same college. Bobby and I were exactly the same age. He was the brother I'd always wanted, and we played together like long lost siblings during the one week allotted to us each summer. Every year we picked up our friendship as if there'd been no interval since the last visit.

Safely ensconced in the Fort's shady solitude, soft drinks and comic books on the wooden floor beside us, we gazed down upon the rooftops of the neighborhood through a shifting curtain of leafy green, pretending we were on the swaying deck of a ship at sea or in the gondola of a fabulous lighter-than-air balloon which was just skimming the treetops. It was easy to shut out the entire world, simply by pulling the canvas flap at the door shut, and sitting cross-legged on the creaking floorboards.

Bobby kicked his legs out over the side. We'd been talking about our just-finished first year of junior high school, and how different it had been from elementary school.

"I don't know about your school, Guy, but it seems that the boys in my school only have one thing on their minds: girls. Yuk."

31

"I know. It seems like that's all they care about anymore. Last year they wouldn't be caught dead talking to them."

"Everybody's changing so much. Getting so stuck up and stuff. I wish we could go back to the days when everybody was reading comic books and trading them."

"Yeah. Those were the good old days. But you can't go back, you know. Changing is normal."

"Oh yeah? Well I don't know about you, but I'm never gonna be any different than I am now."

"Come on, Bobby, not all the changes are bad. There's some that are pretty good."

"Oh? Like what, for instance?"

"You know... "

"No, I don't. What?"

I looked at him. Bobby had always been a late bloomer, a little slow to catch on to things. For all I knew, he might not even have discovered masturbation yet. In order to find out for sure, I started talking about something completely different, but making veiled references to it, weaving phrases like 'doing it', or 'wrist action' or 'shooting off' into my talk, with obvious emphasis. He laughed along good-naturedly, sensing a joke but not quite getting it, with a hint of lostness in his face—and I took a malicious delight in this subtle needling.

"Come on, Guy, what are you laughing about? Are you making fun of me?"

"No. It's just that you're so innocent."

"What's wrong with that? Why should I feel ashamed because I'm not as smart as you? Good grades aren't everything, you know."

"No, dum-dum. I'm talking about the facts of life. Sex and that kind of stuff."

"Oh." He fell silent. "You mean like dirty jokes and stuff. If you want to know the truth, I just don't like those kinds of jokes."

"Maybe it's because you don't get them. If you don't understand the punch line, it won't make any sense to you."

He shook his head vehemently. "No, I mean they're all so stupid. Like this one joke about a man with a ten-foot long dick. It's so long it reaches all the way up to the ceiling. He trains his pet monkey to climb up it but the monkey keeps slipping down. Or something like that. It's a dumb joke." His voice trailed off and he looked truly lost.

"Don't worry, Bobby, it'll come to you someday."

He made a face, then turned to me with a serious expression. "Guy, what's all this about 'beating off'? I heard some guys talking about it once, but they wouldn't tell me."

My suspicion was confirmed: he knew nothing. And it made me feel so superior.

"You mean to tell me you don't *know*?"

He shook his head, big-eyed. "What is it?" he whispered.

I smiled mysteriously with the smug look of one who knows all the secrets of the universe. "Boy, are you dumb."

"Come on, Guy, tell me." Then with a suspicious look on his face: "Do *you* know?"

"Of course I do."

It was delightful to savor the immense gap I felt suddenly yawn between us. Leaning back, I laced my fingers together and cupped my palms behind my head. After peering up through the cracks in the roof at the patterns of leaf and sky beyond, I hesitated for a moment, then said: "You know what? I don't think you know anything about anything."

A worried look crossed his face. "What do you mean?"

"I mean, about sex. Where babies come from. And how babies are made. That kind of stuff."

"Oh, I know all that. We saw a film about it in hygiene class."

"Yeah?"

He shrugged his shoulders. "The woman gets pregnant when the man puts his dick inside her. There was a cartoon explaining it all."

"Yeah, we saw the same thing. What a laugh. The cartoons made it all seem so mechanical, like pieces of a machine fitting together. No mention about how good it feels."

"How do *you* know how it feels?"

"Because it probably feels a lot like beating off."

"Oh." He looked perplexed.

I grew impatient. "Listen, 'beating off' is just another term for masturbation."

"Masturbation?"

"Yes, dum-dum. That's when you make yourself *come*. You know what I mean by 'come', don't you?"

His face fell a little. "Yeah," he said evasively, his voice getting weaker. He seemed to sense that the talk was getting into dangerous territory. "Yeah, I guess I do."

"Do you really?"

"Sure I do."

"Then tell me," I taunted. I saw the look of panic which flitted across his face quickly replaced by an uncertain attempt at casualness. I pressed on: "I bet you never even did it."

"Did what?"

"You know. With yourself."

He hesitated, then—as if offended—shot back, "Sure I did."

"Oh yeah? Then how do you do it?"

"The same way as everybody else, I guess."

"How does everyone do it?"

"I don't know how *every*one does it. You'll have to ask everyone." Then he countered triumphantly: "How do *you* do it, Guy?"

Now it was my turn to hesitate. I was weighing the alternatives: to keep him in the dark and continue to needle him, or to be the one to divulge the mystery, to initiate him into the secret brotherhood. My choice was clear.

"Do you really want to know?"

"Yeah."

"Then listen."

My throat was dry and my stomach felt cool and weighty. I could almost feel Bobby's trembling excitement as if we were linked by invisible sparks jumping across the space between us. I swallowed, then went on in a low voice: "You know how your dick sometimes gets hard and points straight up, like this?" With my index finger, I imitated a penis coming to erection with a series of short, quick jerks.

"Yeah?"

"Didn't you ever touch yourself when it was like that?"

"I guess so."

"I mean," I said impatiently, "touch yourself in the way they call 'beating off'? You know... "

Ringing my fingers around a phantom penis in the air before me I demonstrated with a rapid up-and-down jogging of my wrist.

Bobby's face blanched. He wore a look of awe and horror mixed with fascination, as if he were witnessing something sinful and forbidden. In the silence we could hear the children in the next yard calling and squealing to each other.

I tisked with scorn. "God, I can't believe how dumb you are. All the kids do it. That's what they're talking about. Didn't you *know*?"

He remained silent with a look of queasy stoicism.

"You keep doing it like this, and pretty soon it starts to feel real good. That's when it shoots out."

"It *shoots* out?"

"Yeah." I made a rasping noise with my lips and traced the arc of a trajectory with my finger, landing on his lap.

"Gross!" He drew away in disgust.

"It doesn't feel gross when you're doing it. It feels good."

"How does it feel? Sort of tickle?"

"I can't describe it. It... it's just the best feeling in the world. There's nothing in the world like it. Nothing even comes close." Then with a suggestive grin I added, "Why don't you try it?"

He shook his head and backed away a little. "No way. Forget it." He looked shocked and embarrassed, even slightly sick—and I felt a twinge of cruel delight.

"Do it tonight in the shower," I urged confidentially. "No one can see you."

"No way. I'm not a sissy like you are."

"What do you mean? Everyone does it. Besides... I thought you said you did it, too."

"Not like that," he said in a last desperate attempt to regain his dignity. "I do it different."

"Sure you do... "

"If you don't believe me, I'm leaving."

"Don't worry, I believe you. Who said I didn't believe you?" But the look on my face must have clearly indicated skepticism, for his expression turned defiant. "Okay, Bobby, forget it. I was just kidding you. Come on, let's read these comics. Just like the old days."

"All right."

* * *

That night as I sat on my bed, Bobby came running from the bathroom where he'd been taking a shower. With a look of wild joy on his face, he came bounding over to me like a playful puppy, almost bowling me over in his exuberance. Dancing, laughing, he threw playful punches at my face, slapping and pounding my back so happily that I had to fight him off.

"So you did it, huh?" I said in a low voice.

He denied it vehemently, but his attitude gave him away. He

couldn't keep from jumping up and down.

I pushed him away. "Cut it out." Then I asked in a whisper, "How did it feel?"

"Great!" he shouted. Then in an excited whisper he described how he'd panicked initially at the onset of the strange new feeling, but remembering my words, had continued on until he'd been overwhelmed by the most delicious feeling in the world.

"You should have seen the shower wall! But I didn't even care!"

In his zeal he began illustrating by pumping his fist furiously in front of his pelvis.

"Stop it!" I hissed. "What if someone sees you?"

"Ooops!" He slapped a hand over his mouth and put on a comically contrite look.

"Nothing in the world feels as good, right?"

"Yeah." After he calmed down, he began to talk seriously about certain dreams he'd been having for the past several months. Though he couldn't quite remember their contents, he did have vague, half-forgotten memories of melting bliss. That was what his experience in the shower had reminded him of, and he'd felt an eerie sensation of recapturing that dream feeling.

"It's called a wet dream," I said. "You were coming in your sleep even before you knew what coming was."

"Why does that happen?"

"The pressure builds up if you don't let it out every now and then. It's nature's way of relieving you."

"I always felt a little scared. I didn't even realize I was wetting my pants. It was always dry in the morning."

"At first not much comes out. Then more and more does."

"How come you know so much?"

"I read it in a book called *What Every Boy Should Know*. That book tells you everything. And it's right in the school library, too. Me and Jack are always peeking into it."

"Is that where you learned about beating off?"

"No. I discovered that by accident one day."

"Guy, where do you usually do it?"

"Right here on the bed. About where you're lying."

He quickly shifted away from the spot and I laughed. Then he asked me with a straight face:

"What do you do with your come?"

"When I'm ready to come I roll to the side of the bed and do it onto the floor."

He glanced downward.

"Don't worry, I always clean it up."

"If you do it tonight, be sure and wake me up. That way I can jump out of the way when you're ready to shoot."

"Get lost!"

He laughed and jumped over to his cot. He imitated the motions of jerking off frantically, his face contorted like a monkey's, his throat emitting simian grunts.

From that night on, Bobby's quick pantomime of a jerk-off became a secret signal between us. We did it at each other whenever we thought no one was watching—in the hallway, in the living room, outside. It became a symbol of our giddy, shared joy. And when we were safely unseen, we attacked each other with the gesture, making sputtering noises with our mouths, dirtying each other with the imaginary ejaculate, and afterwards breaking down into helpless, howling laughter, giggling until our sides ached. No one could guess why we were acting so strangely.

Whenever Bobby returned from a trip to the bathroom, I accused him of beating off. He did the same to me. At first we both denied it, but then confessed that the thought of being suspected of it only made us want to do it.

On the fourth day of his visit, we went to see a movie at the Sunnyside Mall. We were sitting in our seats waiting for the feature to start. I was feeling bored and restless, not at all interested in the movie, and I could tell that Bobby, too, had other things on his mind. We fell silent for a long time. Then suddenly we looked into each other's eyes and smiled. Not a word was exchanged. As if at a pre-arranged signal, we rose to our feet and walked up the aisle, back toward the men's room. By the time we got there we were both skipping, barely able to contain our excitement.

The men's room was completely empty, and we took two stalls, side by side.

I'd done it often enough alone in here, but there was something about Bobby's physical proximity that heightened my excitement this time. I was acutely aware of him in the next stall like a twin or alter ego. His sneakers and a bit of pant leg were visible in the lower gap of the partition between us.

"Are your pants down?" I called to him softly.

"No."

"What are you waiting for, dummy?"

I heard the rustle of his pants dropping to the floor, the clink of his belt buckle hitting the tile.

"Okay, I'm ready." His voice echoed slightly in the high-ceilinged restroom.

"Are your briefs off, too?"

"Yes! I'm sitting here buck naked, with a hard-on fit to bust!" His voice trembled, though it was kept discretely low. "What about *you*?"

"I've *been* ready." Indeed I was already fondling myself.

"I can't believe we're doing this, can you?" he whispered. "This is crazy. What if someone came in just now?"

"They wouldn't know what's going on—unless they can see through walls. What are you afraid of?"

I could hear faint sounds from outside, but the roaring in my ears dimmed it out. The speakers installed inside the men's room suddenly crackled into life; the feature was starting, but we didn't care. I heard Bobby smother a giggle, then catch his breath.

It grew silent but for the sound of our breathing—breathing interrupted by our mischievous giggles. I listened to the sighs and catches in Bobby's breaths, timing my own beat to the tiny slaps I could hear whenever his fist hit his groin. It was soon hitting in a steady rhythm. I felt as if we were mentally linked, caught in the same psychic web, our two separate pleasures becoming one.

Then I heard a quick gasp as he sucked in his breath. After what seemed a long, tension-filled interval, I saw, accompanied by the sound of his grunt, the sudden quivering appearance on the floor of the adjacent stall of a small white gob... then another, another—like drops of hot tallow from a candle someone was shaking.

At that sight, I felt my vision get blurred. A heartbeat later, my own offering, identical to Bobby's in every way, joined the floor down between my feet. My heart was pounding furiously, as if I'd just run a sprint. As I tried to catch my breath, I could hear Bobby on the other side of the partition breathing just as hard, a staccato soughing punctuated by the catch of nervous laughter. Amazed at what we'd just done, I gazed down at the irrefutable evidence that Bobby and I were one: we had done the same thing, had felt the same ecstasy at almost the very same moment. And the scattered drops of white on the floor were the perfect seal to our boyhood bond.

* * *

It was the last night of Bobby's stay. We were talking about what we'd done at the theater.

"I can't believe we actually did that, can you?"

"We would probably be locked away if they found out."

"Who's gonna find out?"

He was sitting cross-legged on his cot with his back against the wall, and I could tell he was aroused. I could see the thick lump of his erection under his pajama bottoms, a hardness like a jack-knife. I wondered if he realized how obvious it was. Despite myself, I found my glance stealing downward at his crotch, and he, noting the direction of my glance, brought his knees up in embarrassment.

We found ourselves growing keenly aware of each other's excitement. I saw a trapped look come into his eyes and he began to stammer and swallow.

I tried to turn my thoughts elsewhere, to dampen my own urge, hoping that it would go away. And I knew he was probably doing the same thing. It became almost a competition, an endurance contest. Neither of us wanted to admit to the desire to masturbate. I was waiting for him to weaken and give in, and with a guilty look on his face find some excuse to go to the bathroom... earning my knowing grin—the grin of a victor for the vanquished.

I knew it wouldn't be long now. He had a troubled look on his face. A faint aroma of semen wafted in the air, and I didn't know if it was from him or me. It made me slightly queasy. Then, his eyes glowing, he swallowed hard.

"I have to use the bathroom," he muttered suddenly, getting to his feet.

I grinned.

"It's not what you think," he said. "I really do have to go."

"Sure you do," I said pointedly. "You'd better *go* before you do it in your pants."

His hand was resting on his crotch, unsuccessfully trying to hide the mound thrusting up beneath his pajamas.

"It's not that," he insisted, dropping down to his knees, then onto his stomach, hiding it. "That's all you ever think about." He sounded peeved.

"Why don't you just admit it?" I pressed. "You wanted to beat off, right?"

"Why don't *you* admit it?" His ears were turning red.

I stared at him then made motions of a boy beating off. He

kicked me in the leg. For a long moment we were both silent. When he finally spoke, his voice was little more than a croak.

"So what if I did? Didn't you?"

"Me?"

"Yeah, you. Didn't you feel like it?"

I felt my ears burn.

"You probably wanna do it right now," he said.

I felt as if I were at the start of a roller coaster ride, inching slowly up to the top of the first big hump where the roller coaster is poised briefly, almost at a complete stop, just before the steep, rushing, mind-numbing decline. The roaring in my ears wouldn't go away. My voice sounded funny as I heard myself say: "Okay, then, I'll do it if you do it."

He looked at me in surprise. "What, here?"

"Yeah. What's wrong with that?" Emboldened by the way he flushed scarlet, I pressed on, "Come on, how about it?"

He remained silent. A doubtful look crossed his face. I changed my tactic to one I knew would have a greater effect. "Ah, you're just chicken, that's all."

His face colored some more and I felt my own excitement rise.

"I should have known you'd be too scared," I taunted.

"I'm not, either!"

"You are!"

"I'll do it *if...* " He looked up. "...if you go first. How's that?"

I felt my scalp prickle. The thought of seeing Bobby naked— and not just naked, but with an erection—was getting me excited.

I'd never seen another boy's hard-on, though I'd often noticed the semi-rigid state of some of the boys in the PE showers—a condition which, given the intimacy of the situation, probably couldn't be helped. Such teasing intimations had only made me yearn to see a boy's full erection. My knees were weak and trembly.

It seemed a long time passed before either of us spoke.

Finally, in a strained, weak voice I said, "How about if we do it together?" I shot a silly grin at him.

Looking a little scared, he nodded.

For a few moments we felt weighed down by the heaviness of our decision, unable to say or do anything.

"Well?"

Not wishing to appear scared myself, I initiated the action. Getting to my knees, I slipped my t-shirt over my head, then hesitated with my hand on my pajama bottoms, waiting for him to follow suit.

"Do I have to take my t-shirt off?" he asked.

"Yes." I knew that for him, baring his chest was a major hurdle of inhibition.

Selfconsciously, with an expression of reluctance, he slipped out of his t-shirt, then waited a moment, scratching at a spot just below his left nipple.

"Well?" I said, suddenly nervous myself. "What are you waiting for?"

"I'm not going till you go."

"We'll do it together, then."

Our hands hovered uncertainly about the waist bands of our pajamas. Then, stealing shy glances at each other, we slid our pajamas down and stood bashfully before each other clad only in our white cotton briefs. We snickered nervously, neither willing to take the final step—even though our mutual excitement was outlined in bold diagonal relief under our shorts, only held in check by the elastic waist bands.

"Go ahead," I said breathlessly.

"No, you go. You're first."

"Chicken."

"You're chicken. It was your idea."

"At the same time, then."

"All right."

"One... two... three... go!"

As if racing, we wriggled out of our briefs, kicked them away and straightened up again. At first we both found it difficult to look at one another, to gaze directly at what most drew our attention. Yet neither did we make any attempt to cover up our nakedness. Now that the last barriers of modesty had been removed, we were struck dumb with shyness.

There was a special feeling of intimacy in seeing him naked now, and it was quite different from watching a classmate in PE. In the locker room or the showers, nudity was taken for granted. But here in the privacy of my bedroom another boy's body became also imbued with the 'idea' of nakedness; the necessary prelude to the most private acts a boy could perform: bathing, defecation, or masturbation.

"Well?"

I thought his penis was the biggest one I'd ever seen in my

life, and felt my chest shiver. At the same time I was relieved to see that it looked so much like my own—even down to the swollen veins. It was just as I'd imagined it.

Poking up flat against his stomach, its bulging glans was glowing a deep reddish purple. At the base of the shaft was a wispy patch of light brown hair, much sparser than my own. And hugging the groin tightly were the balls, small and close together, almost as if enclosed in a single sac. A few isolated hairs poked out from them.

My mind was in a daze. I felt light-headed, as if all this were happening in a dream... in some naughty daydream as I sat doodling at my school desk or reclining in my backyard hammock.

"You ever notice how much alike everyone looks?" I said. "I mean, alike in a way, but different in a way."

"Yeah. There's a guy named Mason in my class whose dick is shaped a little weird."

"How do you mean?"

"It's curved a little. All the guys make fun of it behind his back."

I laughed.

"Hey, Guy, is it okay if I touch yours for just a second? I just want to know how it feels."

"Go ahead."

Shyly, he reached out his hand and touched me. At the brush of his finger there was a twitch. We both giggled.

"I can't help it." Under our staring eyes, I felt myself swell up even bigger and stretch to the limit.

Giggling nervously, he continued his exploration. With his mouth slightly open, he traced a vein with his finger. I felt a faint tickle and shut my eyes. When I opened them again he had shifted around, kneeling to examine me closely, his face lowered in eager investigation.

"If you don't watch it," I laughed, "you're gonna get it right in the face!"

"You'd better not!" He jerked his head back, but then brought it cautiously forward to continue his fascinated study.

After a moment I spoke up. "Now let me see yours."

In his turn, he lay back, submitting himself to my exploration. His penis had gone a little soft, but at my first touch, it swelled out again, stiffening with a series of short, quick jerks. I rubbed the glans, marvelling at its smooth velvety feel.

42

"Hey! Don't do that."

It was slightly damp and warm, and I noticed for the first time a tiny clear drop of liquid quivering like a dewdrop on the very tip.

"What's this?"

Curiously I touched it, thinking it was a drop of urine, but when I withdrew my finger it clung and stretched out, following my movements like an elastic goo. I'd never noticed it before on my own.

"Stop it," he said breathlessly.

"Why?"

"You know."

I flushed. Then, to get over the awkward pause by turning it into a joke, I grasped his shaft and began pumping.

"Is this how you do it?"

My heart was pounding so hard I could barely hear my own voice. The feel of Bobby's hardness in my palm was a curious, reversed sensation; the familiar jogging grip in my hand, but with no corresponding visceral response of my own. It was a telescoped, remote excitement, knowing only with my mind what my touches were doing to him.

"Don't."

His face looked flushed and troubled. He shut his eyes and his breathing became disturbed.

I stopped but kept my hand where it was.

"I said cut it out."

I felt his hand push mine firmly away.

"Then touch me again," I commanded in a strange, broken voice.

His startled look showed that he immediately understood the urgency of my request.

Seeing him hesitate, I urged, "Come on." Taking his hand I placed it on my penis, felt it shy back. Then I closed my eyes as I felt the fingers delicately place themselves into position.

The movement was almost imperceptible at first.

"Like this?"

I nodded. "Harder."

My command was obeyed. To my delight I felt him stroke me briskly with the same motions of the wrist, the identical encirclement of the fingers, the exact rhythm I myself employed. The same information had mysteriously been transmitted to each of us through nature's magical network... without the aid of human communication.

A clump of resistance seemed to melt away as my pleasurable sensations grew. I became a fawning slave to his stroking hand. All the muscles in my body went limp and slack, but, like distant peaks being tinted by the dawning sun, separately grew tense.

My resistance broke down; I gave voice to my desire, begging softly: "Take me all the way."

I felt the hand stop.

"Don't stop!" I almost barked, and felt the jog again, the good feel of the jog, and I didn't resist, I couldn't resist, I let go.

"Oh."

Arching my back, clenching my toes, I bucked my pelvis hard against his fist.

Soft warmth kissed my chin... my chest... my cheek...

I lay trembling, listening silently to the repercussions still echoing within my body. When I opened my eyes and turned to look at him, I saw the uneasy look on his face.

"It's okay," I reassured him, "don't worry."

"It's not that... " He was gazing at my body as if seeing it for the first time, a little scared. The expression on his face was that of a boy ready to crumple into tears.

Suddenly he backed away and wordlessly, without looking at me, knelt on the floor and began stroking his penis furiously. He bit his lower lip with an intent look of concentration on his face. I took note of the subtle way he pumped his hips to accentuate the pleasure of his hand's caresses. Quickly his face softened into a pouty moue. The racing speed of his hand became positively comical. He whimpered, grunted, bucked.

With tiny slapping sounds, a scattering of white islands materialized before him, dotting the floorboards, sprinkled out for quite a distance.

After a moment, he turned to look at me and our eyes met. We were both a little shame-faced, but rather than covering up the awkward moment with jokes, we remained silent. I jerked out some tissues from the box at my bedside and handed him the box. Wordlessly, almost grimly, we began cleaning up our messes.

4. Queerbait

I first heard the word at the start of eighth grade as I was taking my books out of my locker one day just before homeroom. A group of boys were nearby, huddled in quiet discussion, and I overheard it said in an undertone. For some reason I looked toward them, alarmed by the suggestive tone of the word.

Some of them looked quickly away before moving off, and I was disturbed, suspecting they'd been whispering something about me. I caught up with one of them, a boy named Richard.

"Hey, Richie, what's up?"

He didn't answer me, but slunk away with a smirk on his face, casting knowing looks toward another boy.

I began to get scared. A feeling of dread sank through me, making my skin prickle. I grabbed him by the arm.

"I said: what's up?"

He heard the desperation in my voice and shrugged off my hand. I felt the blood rush to my face.

"Listen, Richie, you better tell me what's up or I'll pound the crap out of you!"

He grinned at me, and the sight of his pointed cleft chin enraged me still further. "You were walking to school with Mark Warren this morning, weren't you?" he said.

"Yeah, sure. So?"

"So Mark Warren is a faggot, that's what."

"A faggot? What's a faggot?" I had a vision of a small, furry animal, something like a rabbit.

He looked amused at my ignorance. "A queer. A fairy. A homo." He pantomimed grotesquely with a limp wrist. "He likes other boys."

"What?"

I let go of him and watched as he scurried away to join his friends with a backward look of derision. The feeling of dread had now lodged firmly in the pit of my stomach. I was familiar with the term 'homo' which had always been applied to those effeminate sissies whom I'd despised since I was little, but I couldn't understand how it could be used to describe Mark, an attractive boy (easily one of the handsomest boys in school) with whom I'd lately tried to become friends. And certainly it couldn't be applied to *me* just because I'd walked with him to school.

I decided to ask Jack about it. Jack was sure to know; he always had all the answers.

I waited for him in the hallway after first period. This year we had different classes for English, science, and algebra; we shared PE, social studies, and French. He waved his hand when he saw me standing by his locker.

"Hey, Guy, what's up?"

"Jack, listen. Do you know Mark Warren?"

"Yeah, I know who he is. What about him?"

"They say he's a faggot. Is it true?"

He shrugged. "I wouldn't be surprised."

"Why do they call him that?"

He looked at me as if he thought I were testing him, and I felt ashamed at how innocent I must have seemed to him. "Because he likes boys."

"What's wrong with that?"

He shot me a look of contempt, exasperated that he had to explain something so simple. "Don't you know anything? That means he likes to do it with other guys."

"Do what? What do you mean?"

"Stuff like BJs."

"BJs? What are they?"

"Don't you even know what a BJ is? It stands for 'blow job', and it means sucking a guy's dick."

A jolt went through me. "That's disgusting!" I whispered feebly, my throat dry, my voice almost a croak. "That's the sickest thing I ever heard of."

He smiled at my reaction, then turned confidential. "They caught him one time getting a hard-on in the PE showers."

"No!"

"It's true. Bill Jenkins and a couple of other guys beat the shit out of him for it."

"Just for getting a hard-on? But Jack... does that make him a faggot? I mean, it might have been a mistake. It could happen to anyone by accident, couldn't it?"

"Not to him."

"How can you say that for sure?" I was almost begging. "Besides, it might be a lie that he got a hard-on. 'Cause I don't think Mark Warren would do... what you just said."

Jack had his hands thrust deep inside his jacket pockets. As he contemplated my bewilderment, a mysterious grin lit up his face. "You don't know anything, do you?"

"What do you mean?"

"There's a lot worse things than blow jobs."

"A lot worse—?"

"Wanna know what else they do that's even more disgusting?"

"What?"

He looked around to see that we weren't being overheard before whispering: "They like to take it up the ass."

"What does that mean, 'take it up the ass'?"

"Well, Guy-baby, it means getting fucked in the butt."

I felt the blood drain rapidly from my face. "Those faggots!" A black cloud of terror swelled up in my chest, almost choking my breath and making me feel weak and faint. I didn't notice that Jack had circled around behind me until I felt two hands firmly planted on either side of my hips.

"What are you doing, Jack?"

"Can't you tell? This is how they do it."

"Do what?"

I twisted around to try to see over my shoulder, but knew immediately from the soft bumps against my butt what Jack was doing. "Cut it out, Jack!" A feeling of panic came over me.

"Don't you like it, Guy-baby?"

"Don't call me Guy-baby!"

Why was he doing this to me? I tried to fight him off. "Please, Jack, don't! It's not funny!"

Like a strange, demented demon, he would not be budged; a look of savage fury glinted in his eyes.

"Stop it!" I screamed.

I felt him let go, then watched him skip away down the hall. "See you later, Guy!" he called from the other end as if nothing had happened.

My knees were trembling and my forehead damp with sweat as I watched him disappear around the corner.

All that morning I couldn't concentrate in my classes. Instead, I looked forward impatiently to lunch period, when I would be able to go to the school library and confirm what I'd heard.

After hurriedly bolting down my lunch, I rushed to the library.

Miss Thompson, the librarian, smiled at me from behind the check-out counter.

"Hello, Guy."

"Hi, Miss Thompson."

I went straight to the stacks to find the book I'd so often pored over in secret: *What Every Boy Should Know*, a slim green volume shelved next to its companion volume in red, *What Every Girl Should Know*. I looked up 'homosexuality' in the index and turned to the page indicated. It was in the chapter dealing with hygiene, and there was a disappointing half-page devoted to the topic:

> 'Homosexuality' is the term given to an aberration in which a man's normal feelings for a female are misdirected and re-channeled toward another male. In adolescence, when young people's bodies are changing, and there is much curiosity, it is normal for friends of the same sex to indulge in mutual explorations. In fact, it is quite common for a boy to develop romantic attachments to another of the same sex. Such attachments may often be quite intense, and even lead to consummation. There is no need to be alarmed in such a case. Most boys soon grow out of this phase and learn to direct their feelings toward girls.
>
> But when this feeling for other boys persists, it develops into a condition known as 'homosexuality' (from the Greek word, *homo*, meaning 'same'). In most cases, this condition weakens and disappears as one gets older, except in those rare cases in which it persists into adulthood. Because these adults retain their child-like behavior, never growing out of the adolescent stage, most psychologists consider homosexuality to be a form of mental illness. There are divergent opinions as to how prevalent this condition is in our society...

I replaced the book on the shelf feeling faint and sick, thinking of some of the things I'd done with Bobby last summer. Certainly they would have to qualify as 'mutual explorations', even though I'd thought of them primarily as extensions of my own self-pleasure.

Was it an accident that Mark Warren seemed drawn to me? But how was I to know about him? There had been no indication, no warning sign... After a moment's reflection, the horrible truth dawned on me. The way he carried his books (cradled on his forearms), the way he walked (with short, quick steps which made his bottom wiggle): these were unmistakable signs, and if only I'd been more observant, I'd have noticed them right away.

Now my classmates had lumped me together—albeit accidentally—with those pale sissies whom I despised perhaps more than any of them.

I kept thinking of the phrase 'this condition disappears as one gets older'. That could only mean that it was, after all, a passing phase I was going through. Perhaps many other boys had also gone through it. One thing was for sure, though: it would never happen again. I thought of Jack's face when he'd explained what a faggot was, and felt a choking, murderous anger well up in my breast.

"Did you find what you were looking for?" Miss Thompson was smiling warmly as I walked past the check-out desk.

"Yes."

* * *

Mark was waiting for me by my locker at the end of the day. I didn't notice him at first because of the crowd of students milling in the hallway.

"Guy."

When I turned to look, I saw him standing there with a hurt look on his face. "What do you want?" I said.

"Where have you been?"

"In my classes." I had steered clear of him all day, pretending not to see him, avoiding the places where we usually met.

"What's the matter?" he asked.

"Nothing's the matter. Why do you ask?"

"It sort of seems like you're trying to avoid me for some reason."

"Why should I try to avoid you?"

"I don't know. It just seems that way, that's all."

"I just want to be alone, okay? I want to be by myself."

"How come?"

"Do I have to have a reason? I just want to, that's all. Anyway, who says I have to have permission from you? Do I have to tell you everything?"

"Wait, Guy—"

"Let go of my elbow."

He had grabbed me lightly as I turned to go, and for some reason that light touch felt like an unclean caress. When he saw the look on my face, he actually cringed.

"Let go, damn it!" I tugged myself loose and pushed my way through the crowd, fighting free of his imagined clasp. I could feel him staring after me. Suddenly I was running, baffled and angry.

At the steps of the main entrance I ran into Jack as he was strapping his bookband around his textbooks. Though he didn't notice me at first, something told me he'd just seen me talking with Mark.

"Jack, wait up."

He began bounding down the steps, three at a time, his books slung over his shoulder.

I caught up with him and matched my steps to his. "Where you going?"

"To see Sheri." This was his current girlfriend, Sheri Drennon. Since entering junior high school, Jack had already gone steady with half a dozen girls, a school record. (No one else even came close.) Sheri was a freckle-faced redhead who'd been in my class last year, a rather wild girl who was always in trouble with the teachers. In fact, she'd been sent home from school this morning for wearing a too-short skirt to homeroom.

To me she wasn't very attractive and I was a little disappointed that Jack had chosen her from among all the other more attractive girls—it lowered him just the slightest bit in my estimation. Still, she was, as Jack whispered in my ear as we walked up her driveway, 'stacked'.

She greeted us at the door chewing gum, and I was reminded of the time our teacher had caught her chewing gum in class and had made her put the wad on the end of her nose.

Nobody else was home so we went into the living room and chatted idly for a while. Jack and Sheri were seated close together on the sofa, and I couldn't help noticing the proprietary way Jack put his arm around her. I envied the ease with which he did everything.

Soon he was nuzzling her cheek and sneaking light kisses until, with a sigh almost of resignation, Sheri finally returned a kiss. The silences in the conversation grew longer as their kisses became prolonged... while I sat before them, my rapt attention tinged with awkwardness.

Oblivious to my presence, they were hugging in the most intimate way and nibbling at each others' mouths. Their kisses sounded viscid and liquid and quite erotic, and I was growing weak with longing. There was a keen smell of something in the close room. I saw Jack's hand slide up and boldly fondle one of Sheri's breasts. She made a halfhearted remonstration, pushing his hand away and glancing modestly toward me (I quickly put on an air of nonchalance). But when she returned to her kissing I continued my absorbed study.

It seemed that my presence, far from dampening her ardor, only emboldened and inflamed her kisses to an alarming degree. A suggestive movement below caught my attention. It was Jack rocking himself furtively against her thigh. I felt light-headed, almost faint. Couldn't she feel it?

Perhaps she did, for just then she pulled away from the kiss and sat up straighter.

"My mom'll be coming home soon. You better go." Her voice sounded strained. She shook the hair out of her eyes.

"Oh, we got time," mumbled Jack in a hoarse voice.

"You know I'm on restriction. If she catches you here, she'll kill me."

"Oh, all right." Jack made no secret of his disappointment. "Come on, Guy, let's go. It's getting too *dan*gerous for some people around here."

"Jack... don't take it like that," she said.

I was trying to keep my eyes away from Jack's crotch, almost dreading the thought of what I would see there.

"Let's go, Guy."

Outside, the bright sunlight was so dazzling that we had to stand still for a moment, blinking weakly before continuing on. I hadn't realized how dark it was in the living room with its curtains drawn.

"What do you think of her?" asked Jack after a while.

"Sheri? She sure lives up to her reputation."

He gave me a funny look. "She's a cock-tease, that's what she is: a cock-tease. All she wants to do is get you hot."

"But she let you cop a feel."

"Aw, sometimes a little tit now and then but never below the waist."

"Wow." I loved it when Jack talked like this, using the dirty words that high school boys used. It felt so grown-up.

"Girls sure are weird," he said. "I can't figure them out."

"What do you mean?"

"Well, take Sheri, for instance. She'll let you kiss and kiss her, and even cop some tit, but that's it. You saw the way she was. She loves to be watched—to kiss in front of other people. Girls are like that. They pretend to be shy, but really they want it just as much as you do."

"How can you tell?"

"Their lips get real hot. That means they're hot down there."

I had to swallow once before I could ask the next question. "Do you think she'll ever let you go all the way?"

He gave me a quick glance which I was unable to decipher, then looked down at his feet, kicked a rock away into the bushes.

"I dunno," he said out of the side of his mouth.

Feeling emboldened, I pressed on: "Jack? How do you think it feels to fuck a girl? I bet it feels a whole lot better than beating off."

He turned to look at me with a scornful expression. "You mean you still like to beat off?" he asked, amused.

"No." I blushed. "I ain't no faggot."

He pinched his cheek with his thumb and forefinger and jiggled a loose flap of skin rapidly in and out, making a 'snick-snick-snick' sound whose rhythm was an unmistakable reference to my habits.

"Hey, cut it out, Jack."

"I thought you were Mark Warren's boyfriend."

"Come on, Jack," I said, feeling my ears burn.

* * *

From that night, I began exploring a whole new world, a world which somehow seemed strangely familiar, as if I'd stepped into a garden I'd often seen in my dreams.

Blow jobs? I'd sometimes fantasized about having my penis kissed by another boy, or about kissing another boy's penis. But because I'd thought I was the only one in the whole world who daydreamed about such things, my fantasy had had an almost abstract quality. Never would I have guessed that other boys also thought about it—and not only thought about it, but actually *did* it.

Taking it up the ass? Not even in my wildest dreams had such a thing entered my mind. True, I often experienced a languorous, sensual feeling during a bowel movement. I'd never confessed to anyone how good it felt because it seemed so dirty, the very definition of 'nasty'. Now I realized that others felt it, too.

But I'd never made the obvious connection: that an erect penis was about the same size as what came out. Why hadn't I seen it before? Such a treacherous coincidence... and provided so temptingly by nature.

It was only now as I imagined the pleasure that it gave both parties that the 'why' part of my question—why boys became homosexual—was answered. It was to indulge in this nasty little delight, something which decent people tried to suppress from their minds. No wonder the book in the library couldn't go into details about the 'child-like' activities of homosexuals.

I was disgusted, but simultaneously felt a sort of relief... because the things I'd done last summer with Bobby, which had tormented me so much, were nothing—less than nothing!—compared to what real faggots did with each other.

I got up from my bed now and listened at my bedroom door. The whole house was quiet. Stealthily, I slid the lock into place and crept back to my bed. Earlier in the day, I'd secreted my mother's small hand-held mirror in my bureau drawer. I got it out now. I noticed my hands trembling slightly as I held it.

Feeling like a criminal (and stimulated by the excitement of doing something absolutely forbidden) I slipped out of my pajama bottoms and lay back on my bed. By bending my head and angling the mirror, I could see my own anus for the first time in my life. I spread apart my butt cheeks and exposed to plain view the creasy pink pucker of every boy's most secret spot. No wonder I'd never paid any attention to it before: it was in such an out-of-the-way place that it was invisible except as a reflection in a mirror. I ran a finger gently over it and winced at the unexpected surge of pleasure which swept through me.

That delicate tickle revealed its extraordinary sensitivity. Again I brushed it softly. A tiny, clear pearl quivered on the tip of my sudden erection. Because I was doing something so forbidden, I felt an exciting mixture of fascination, disgust, and guilt.

I dropped the mirror to the floor and closed my eyes the better to concentrate upon my sensations. Delicately I tested with my finger to see if I could probe inside. The feel of my finger pushing against the barrier was delicious beyond words. That finger was like a saucy tongue kissing, teasing, and tickling me to madness.

I realized that I'd stumbled upon another mysterious little world which had lain hidden until now. Just as when I'd first discovered masturbation, I felt like an explorer. I wondered how it would feel if my finger were to penetrate it... I wanted it... Perhaps a lubricant of some kind would ease entry.

I thought of the jar of cold cream I'd borrowed from my mother for my chapped skin. It was sitting on top of the dresser, just within reach from where I was. I unscrewed the cap and dipped a finger into it... and winced at the cool kiss as I dabbed it gently onto my hole. It made a crackling sound as I applied it more liberally, spreading it around and around. Gingerly, delicately, I probed with a finger, my closed eyes giving a detached objectivity to my actions.

My heart leaped when I felt the first tight bite which signalled that the tip of my pinky had finally edged inside. But for a while, pain forbid any further exploration.

I brought my finger up to my nose and caught a bouquet, not the one I expected, but a new, sharp, musky tang which made my stomach trembly and weak with its promise of forbidden pleasures.

Night by night, I found I could manage to get further and further inside with each new try. Instinctively I learned how to relax, to get into the lazy, sensual frame of mind I assumed whenever I sat on the toilet. At first I was worried because the feeling was so much like the other thing—with its heavy, delicious feel in the pit of the stomach. And sometimes I had to wipe away dirty streaks from my finger. But soon I became inured to the sensation, knowing that what I feared wouldn't happen, and just concentrated on enjoying the deceptive—but absolutely safe—sensation of imminent disaster.

As soon as I learned how to slide in quite easily, I used two fingers, then three, stretching my pain threshold to greater limits. But this wasn't enough like 'the real thing'. I thought of another object I could use in place of my fingers, something long and cylindrical... an empty bottle... a carrot... a banana...

Late one night, after everyone was asleep, I crept down to the kitchen and got a banana from the refrigerator. Surely there was nothing odd about a growing boy having a late-night snack...

Back in my room I excised the banana's hard tip with my Boy Scout knife, then coated it carefully with Vaseline, which I'd discovered was a more practical lubricant than cold cream.

With one hand, I pulled off my pajama bottoms and my briefs, then lay back on the bed, giving myself up to my fantasies...

Completely naked upon the bed I was a beautiful young girl with her hands tied behind her back, helpless, about to be forcefully violated. "No... no... don't!" I moaned softly, feeling the ravisher already nudging at the rim (coated beforehand with a slick layer of Vaseline). But at the first slow thrust I felt myself let go, copiously, without the need to touch myself at all.

"Oh!"

I blinked, and felt a single teardrop trickle out the corner of my eye, slip down my temple.

"Oh... "

I lay still for a long time afterwards. It seemed odd that the house could remain so silent after I'd just felt the whole earth convulse.

Finally, I stirred. 'So this is why the fags do it,' I thought to myself. 'No wonder they like it so much.'

A lone cricket chirped from somewhere out in the yard.

5. The Music Lesson

Fads came and went with a dizzying rapidity in junior high. All of a sudden, it seemed, all the boys in our class were goosing each other like crazy. I don't know how it got started, but one day while I was in line at the cafeteria, a boy named Todd sneaked up on me from behind and gave my balls a quick squeeze. I yelled out in surprise, almost spilling the glass of milk on my tray.

Before long we were all greeting each other by making playful grabs at the genitals—in the locker room, in class, in the hallway. It was a boyish assertion of masculinity done in imitation of our older brothers. In a way it was also a gauge of popularity, for the most liked, most envied boys were also the most frequent victims.

I was delighted to discover that the quietest boys would let out loud surprised squawks when I squeezed them. And the playful grabbing gave me a legitimate chance to do something I'd always dreamed of: touching other boys' penises.

I couldn't have been the only one who had this interest, for all the boys were beginning to make jokes and references to each other's penis size. Under cover of the game I was able to touch as many boys as I wanted. However, I was shy about doing it to the boys I really liked.

There was one group of boys who were significantly left out of the sport: the 'sissies', those effeminate, mincing boys who walked like girls and fluttered their hands when they talked. Ever since I was a kid I'd felt an instinctive dislike of them, for there was something about them that was extremely distasteful, though I couldn't say exactly what. Now I began to notice them more and more, perhaps because they conspicuously avoided the rough-housing of the other boys. Whenever I saw the way they carried their schoolbooks—cradled against their chests like girls, not slung low at their sides like most boys—I felt a vague sense of shame.

Mark Warren was the worst of them. Many boys made fun of his mannerisms, and, egged on by Richard and other classmates, almost against my will, I found myself beginning to bully him. At first I was disgusted by the malicious, vicarious delight of the other boys as they stood by watching me do it, but soon the perverse pleasure of seeing Mark humiliated became a source of gratification for me as well. It got to the point where, if I spotted him, I couldn't pass up the chance to do something. Now my audience expected it of me.

For example, if I saw him in the lunchroom, I stalked over to where he sat and, standing impudently before him, calmly shook salt over his pudding or his sliced peaches, staring at him all the while, daring him to tell the teacher on duty (which he never did).

Or I would bring my own tray along and scoop my uneaten peas and salad into his roast beef and potatoes, then stir up the batch into an unpalatable mess, commanding him to eat it. At such times I felt a hot lump in my chest which remained there long after my delighted classmates had pounded me on the back in glee. I was haunted by the fact that he never made a move to fight back, only staring up at me with eyes that begged silently for me to leave him alone.

Whenever I humiliated Mark I felt a satisfaction afterwards that was almost sensual. What made it even more gratifying was the knowledge that every time I bullied him in front of the others, the act helped wipe out the memory of the whispered word I'd overheard by the lockers that day. Perhaps even now my classmates had forgotten that they'd ever said that word about me.

Mark now began to haunt my life in much the same way I haunted his. In our symbiotic tormentor-victim relationship, I felt I needed Mark to prove my own strength, to win the respect I craved. If a girl sometimes remonstrated with me, I always had a ready reply which justified my bullying in the eyes of all my comrades: "Don't you know he's a fag?"

The strange thing was that I had a feeling my attentions were neither undesired nor unappreciated. The martyred look which came over Mark's face made him heartmeltingly attractive, as if smoldering fires within him were being ignited by my cruel attentions...

If only he had ignored me from the start or had told a teacher, I would have stopped terrorizing him. But it was too late now—it was like an addiction. The way I could make his face turn pale with fear or crumple to the point of tears was a temptation I could no longer resist. And because he co-operated so well, I knew he was virtually asking to be pursued and bothered. Otherwise he would have done something about it.

As time passed, most of the other boys left off pestering him, probably under the influence of the girls in class who came to his defense. While this had only increased their cruel joy in the beginning (because it got the girls' attention, which was what they really wanted), eventually it had its effect. In time, I found myself alone in my sport.

It felt strange to have such a diabolical hold over him. If he had wanted to fight me one-on-one, it was by no means impossible for him to make a good showing; he wasn't a thin weakling, but actually quite well-built. But he seemed to fear me to an unreasonable degree. For me, his cringing cowardice only confirmed the rumors about him, and in my contempt, I felt I had to punish him for making his former overtures of friendship to me.

One afternoon, near the beginning of spring term, I spotted him standing in the hallway chatting with a girl. As our eyes met, a strange change came over his face and posture, as if a wave of dread had transformed his very metabolism. The girl noticed it and turned around to see the cause. Emboldened by Mark's show of weakness, I continued to glare at him and didn't break my stride. As I neared him he panicked and broke away, walking rapidly in the opposite direction.

I began pushing my way past the kids in the hallway to get at him. Just then he looked back, almost as if he could sense my pursuit. His walking picked up speed and he began to run. I sprinted after him and managed to catch his sleeve and drag him back into the hall just as he was going through the double doors leading to the principal's office. He tried to shrug free but I shoved him roughly back through the entrance of the boys' room, pinning him against the wall.

An excitement hotter than blood pounded in my chest when his scared face snapped forward and our eyes locked.

"Tell me, faggot," I said with my voice lowered, trembling in spite of myself, "is it true that you like to take it up the ass?"

His face froze. Then, with a calmness which surprised me, he muttered, "Why don't you leave me alone?" and tried to push his way past my encaging arm.

I grabbed him by the elbow and pulled him back into a niche formed between the washroom partition and the urinals. His eyes grew big with fright, belying his recent show of bravado, and I felt a quick spark of relief shoot through me.

"Listen," I hissed between my teeth. "You'd better not sass back if you know what's good for you."

"Why? What are you gonna do about it?"

I was at a loss for an answer and my confidence suddenly ebbed. I wondered again about my ability to take him on in a fight, one-on-one. He had an almost smug look on his face, as if he were laughing at something I couldn't see behind my back. (I actually turned around to see if someone was behind me.) I'd never seen him this confident before.

"How come you're so cocky today?"

"I'm not cocky." His expression changed suddenly, as if in demonstration of this, into a softer one tinged with obsequiousness.

"You are cocky. You're a cocky little faggot, that's what you are."

He glared silently.

"Well? Say something. You're scared, aren't you?"

I shook him roughly, but he didn't reply.

"Listen," I said, my voice pitched low. "You'd better be in the music room after school today if you know what's good for you."

"Why?"

"Just be there if you don't want me to beat the crap out of you."

I let go of him and watched him scurry off. Then, drawn by a confused yearning, I stepped into the hall to watch him walk away. I noted the way his buttocks pressed tightly against the fabric of his pants. To my shame, I found myself picturing how he'd look naked.

* * *

I was first clarinettist in the school band, which automatically made me Mr. Seth's student assistant. I'd been 'volunteered' to keep the music sheets in order, neatly filed by song title and instrument in the music library. I'd also been given the keys to the music room so I could let students in after school to practice for the year-end band festival.

As I made my way to the music room, I spotted a waiting figure by the door. It pleased me to see Mark so compliant after his cheekiness earlier. But when I got closer, I saw it was a girl named Sharon, a fellow band member. Scrawny and stoop shouldered, she was hugging her clarinet case tightly to her chest.

"Hi," she smiled shyly, trying to hide the silver braces on her teeth as much as possible. She had greasy-looking hair parted on one side, and her enlarged eyes peered owlishly from behind the magnifying lenses of her tortoiseshell glasses. I knew—to my embarrassment—that she had a crush on me. Our hands had brushed once as I'd reached to turn the music sheet (she was second-chair clarinet), and she looked so wrought up I thought she'd faint. On another occasion she had sat at the same table with me in the lunchroom, but had been unable to speak a single word, blushing through the whole meal.

I felt flattered by any attention I received from attractive girls, but the fawning looks cast my way by girls like Sharon only shamed me.

"Hi," I said. "Did you wait long?"

"No."

I unlocked the door and we entered the deserted building. She went straight for her usual seat and immediately sat down, opening her case and starting to put her instrument together. Seeing this, I felt obliged to practice with her. Since I hadn't brought my own clarinet with me today, I went into the instrument room to borrow one of the school's.

This instrument room was a separate room within the building with its own locked door to protect its contents from theft. Here, from among the racks of moldy-smelling instrument cases, broken drums, and tarnished tubas, I pulled a clarinet case off a shelf and returned to the outer room. Sharon was already fingering her keys silently as she squinted at the music sheet on the stand. I sat down next to her and began assembling my instrument.

"Do you practice a lot at home?" I asked her.

She nodded.

"Why'd you decide to come here today?"

"I thought everyone would be here."

I looked at her and saw the archetype of the unpopular girl who desperately wants to be one of the crowd. Her weak face seemed to sum up the character of her whole dreary life, and I felt depressed.

"Maybe some other people will turn up," I said in a small, hopeful voice.

The door opened and we both looked up to see Mark Warren standing uncertainly in the doorway.

"Well, look who's here," I said with relief.

Mark stared at Sharon in puzzlement, then transferred his

perplexity to the room at large as his gaze shifted about the clutter of chairs and music stands, to the white soundproof tiles on the ceiling.

"What's the matter?" I said. "Is this the first time you've seen the band room?"

As Mark wandered over to where we were sitting, I was angered at what I thought was an amused smirk on his face as he glanced from Sharon to me. Sharon's unattractiveness was a humiliation for me, though our being together was an accident.

"Why didn't you ever go out for band, Warren?" I asked. Then, as he shrugged noncommittally, I went on: "... because I hear you can *blow* so well."

"Oh?" Sharon perked up and flashed a smile, momentarily forgetting her metal-studded teeth in her relief at being able to join the conversation. "Really? What instrument do you play?"

"The flute," I quickly put in, thinking of the 'skin flute' of boys' jokes. I was delighted at the way Mark's face darkened. "And they tell me he's *so* good. Of course he practices a lot."

"Oh really? How old were you when you first started?" asked Sharon. When Mark didn't answer, she offered helpfully, "*I* started when I was nine. It's supposed to be the earlier you start, the better."

No answer. As she looked from Mark to me, she began to sense that something beyond her comprehension was going on. Hesitantly she continued, "Why don't you practice together with us?"

"No," I said, "he doesn't like to play in front of people. It makes him nervous. He likes to play with himself."

"What do you want?" Mark turned fiercely upon me. "Why did you call me here?"

"I did not call you here," I said quietly. I turned to Sharon. In her oblivion, she was sitting with her mouth slightly open, a blank look on her face. "Sharon, me and Mark want to practice alone."

She continued to look blank for a moment before snapping out of it. (It was the first time I had called her by her first name.) "Oh... " She began to move. "Of course. I'll just... "

While she bustled about, Mark and I were silent. But as soon as she left, Mark turned to me. "Why do you say these things?"

"What things?"

"You know."

"She didn't know what I was talking about. She's dumb."

"Oh, I don't believe this." He looked tired.

For a moment I had a twinge of regret. Perhaps he was innocent. The idea that he could be homosexual suddenly seemed the least likely thing in the world. But if he were stripped of this special status now, I knew I'd lose one of my chief delights. I willed myself into greater cruelty:

"Come on, everyone knows you're a faggot."

"Stop calling me a faggot!" he almost screamed.

"I'm calling you a faggot 'cause that's what you are: a faggot. What's the matter? Truth hurts, huh?"

A look of weary resignation came into his face. "When will you leave me alone?"

"Never. Not till you admit the truth."

"I am not... what you think I am, and I don't know where you got the idea. Some guy might have started that rumor but that's just what it is: a rumor. He was only doing it to be mean. I don't know why."

"I don't wanna argue with you. See that room?" I pointed to the instrument checkout room. "Step in there for a second."

"Why should I?"

"Because I'm afraid you'll run away while I put away this clarinet."

"I won't run away."

"Like hell you won't."

"I promise."

"I don't believe in fags' promises."

He gave an exasperated sigh.

I stood up so suddenly that my chair fell over with a bang. "If you don't step into there right now, I'm gonna have to make you do it."

After a brief look of defiance, he moved toward the room, muttering under his breath, "I don't believe this."

I followed close behind. As I shut the door behind me I felt a whoosh at my ears; the tiny room felt close and packed now that it was air-tight. My ears felt stopped-up. I watched him reading the owners' names stencilled on the various instrument cases.

"What instrument goes in here?" he asked, pointing.

"That's a trombone case." I clicked the door-lock shut and he whirled around at the sound.

"Why'd you do that?"

I stared at him but said nothing. Then I pulled a high stool just in front of the door and sat upon it. Setting my case aside I began to play a slow, seductive melody in the lower register which sounded vaguely exotic... Arabian or Persian... stripper music.

"What are you doing? I don't want to sit here and listen to you play."

I pulled the mouthpiece away. "I'm staying here until you admit the truth."

"Which is?"

"That you really are a faggot."

"Then it looks like we'll be here forever, because I'm not going to tell a lie."

I shrugged and continued playing. As I did so, I watched him feigning nonchalance, studying the different instruments. Soon I felt a warm drop of spit on the inside of my knee where the bell of my instrument rested. I stopped playing. He looked up.

"Well? Are you ready to go home, Mark?"

"I've *been* ready."

"Then admit it."

"Never."

"That's okay. We have all the time in the world for you to change your mind. No one knows we're in here. Nobody."

"That girl knows we're in here."

"She thinks we're practicing together. And even if she came back, when she sees no one in the band room, she'll think we left."

He fell silent, then retreated to the far corner of the musty, closet-like room to be as far away from me as possible. I began taking the clarinet apart and putting the pieces away carefully into the yellow velour-lined compartments inside the case.

First, I unscrewed the metal clamp on the mouthpiece which held the reed in place, then detached the reed and slipped it into a tiny cardboard sleeve provided for it. Instinctively I put the black plastic mouthpiece into my mouth again. I froze. An idea came into my head which made me giggle. Clarinet players learn instinctively to wet their mouthpieces with their saliva, and that was what brought the idea into my head.

"Mark, look."

Keeping my eyes fastened upon his, I smiled wickedly and moved the mouthpiece slowly and sensuously in and out of my mouth. I was gratified to see that even in the dim light of the room, his face, half in shadow, was flushing furiously.

I let him plainly see the visible play of my tongue as it curled and licked. I murmured naughtily, "Mmm."

"Cut it out, Willard."

"What's the matter? Brings back memories?"

"That's not it and you know it."

"Here," I said suddenly, extending the mouthpiece to him. "Show me how it's done. Show me how a real faggot does it."

"Go to hell!"

I slid down off my stool and advanced threateningly toward him. He cowered back into the corner as far as he could go. I brought the mouthpiece up. "Do it," I commanded.

Glaring, he took it and stood for a moment, staring questioningly at me. I made a threatening gesture which made him bring it up to his mouth.

"Do it!" I commanded again, and smiled to see his lips curl distastefully as the mouthpiece slid into his tiny mouth.

He pulled it out, wiping at his lips. "Now can I go home?"

"Not as good as the real thing, huh?"

"I don't know what you're talking about. I really don't. If I'm not home for dinner soon, my mom's gonna wonder where I am. And when I—"

"Shut up! You're not going anywhere until you admit you're a faggot. It's so easy. All you have to do is say, 'I'm a fag.' Then I'll let you go."

"Just like that? No way."

"I don't know why you're being so stubborn. Just repeat after me: 'I am a faggot.' And then you can be on your way."

"I'm not a faggot and that's all there is to it. You can't keep me here like this—"

"Come on, you can say it."

"............."

"I am a faggot," I prompted.

He fidgeted with his hands, passing the mouthpiece from one hand to the other. I reached for it.

"Here, give it back."

As I was replacing it into the case I remembered something else, and a smile spread over my face. I reached behind the little check-out desk and fumbled open the top drawer. From among the little odds and ends within I drew out a small round can which I rolled playfully around in the palm of my hand.

"Do you know what this is for?"

I smiled as I uncapped it and dipped a finger into the opal-hued jelly within. It was the Vaseline used by woodwind players to lubricate the cork linings of their instruments to ease their fitting together. I pulled two parts—the barrel and the mouthpiece—out of the case again, then slowly, deliberately, spread the Vaseline onto the cork linings, studying Mark's face all the while.

"You dab some on here like so. And around here." I twisted one piece slowly into the other. "That way it slides right in."

His eyes widened in shock and I felt a delicious thrill keen through me. I thought to myself wildly: He knows! He knows exactly what's going on!

"Isn't it neat? It's called Vaseline. What a handy invention, huh?"

He was silent.

"Well?"

"All right, all right," he said resignedly.

"What's the matter?"

"If I say that phrase, will you let me go?"

"Of course. That's what I've been saying for the past thirty minutes, isn't it?" There was something in his expression which indicated he'd had enough, and I was secretly regretful that our little game was to end so soon. I'd begun to enjoy myself and was hoping it would last longer.

He sighed loudly. "Okay, okay." He put his hands on his hips and mouthed the phrase distastefully, in a tired, almost sarcastic tone of voice: "'I am a faggot.' Now can I go?"

"Say it one more time, like you really mean it."

"I am a faggot."

"You see how easy it is? Nothing to it, right? Doesn't it feel good to finally let the truth out? Don't you feel cleaner now?"

"You said I could go if I said it."

"Right. So go. I'm not stopping you." I shrugged nonchalantly but remained seated on my high stool just in front of the door.

He was cautious. "I can't go with you there."

"There's plenty of room to go around. I won't touch you. What's the matter, scared?"

There was a silence. Then he began to inch forward, his eyes never leaving my face. When he was within two feet of me, he made a mad dash for the door.

I don't know what happened after that. There was a loud

clatter and a ferocious, hot excitement pounding within me. Mark was in my arms struggling to get free. I shoved him back toward the far corner, kicking the high stool out of the way, slamming against the instrument racks. I felt possessed of a superhuman strength, as though every muscle in my body was charged with energy. My body was acting without the least volition on my part.

"Let me go!"

"Shut up! You little queer!" I gulped down air frantically between ragged gasps. Mark's face was completely unrecognizable, petrified with fright. His mouth gaped open in unbelieving horror.

"What are you gonna do? Let go of my arm!" His voice had slipped into the whining plea of a girl, which made me want to slap his red, wrinkled face.

"Fag, you make me wanna puke, you know that?"

"So what do you want me to do about it?" He tugged his arm in an attempt to pull it away but I only tightened my grip.

"I want you to give me a BJ."

It took a moment for the words to register, and when they did I realized dimly that it was I myself who had spoken them. I was shocked. But it was too late to recall them. They hung in the air and rang echoing inside my mind. My grip on his arm loosened, went slack. I let go.

He made no move to run away. His face registered shocked disbelief.

"You heard me," I said weakly. "Isn't that what you like to do?"

A strange metamorphosis came over his face. The shock had transformed itself into a sneer, and I became scared.

"You mean right here? Right now?"

"Right now," I whispered, my mouth dry.

"You can't make me." He looked toward the door.

"Don't tell me you're scared, faggot. Want me to kick your ass?" But my threat sounded almost like pleading. I was frightened because he seemed so unafraid.

"You're the one who's scared," he said softly.

I heard his voice as if it came through a long narrow tube stuffed with cotton wool. I still couldn't believe what we were discussing.

His face looked drawn and pale, strangely uneasy. My head felt light, and the whole situation became unreal, like something in a dream which only distantly concerned me.

"Come on," I whispered, "Nobody'll ever know."

"We'll be caught here."

"Why? The door's locked."

And then it dawned on me that he had meant that last remark. I felt my heart begin to race so fast I could barely breathe. Little shivers ran along every part of my body. I was trembling like a leaf.

He was looking around in a vaguely criminal way.

I took a step back, not taking my eyes from his face. I couldn't believe that it might actually happen. People didn't really do that kind of thing. It was only a fantasy... a joke.

Still not looking at me, he took a step in my direction.

As if fighting back a choke I managed to say, "Don't tell me you really mean it."

He halted. A frantic kaleidoscope of emotions played across his face at lightning speed, making my stomach churn.

"You really meant it, didn't you?" I insisted. "You were serious."

"No, I wasn't."

"You were, you were. I could tell just now."

"I was not, either!"

I almost jumped with glee. A mad excitement filled me, and I laughed aloud, pointing at him. "Faggot! Wait till I tell the others!" I felt an unearthly happiness well up inside me, a happiness akin to a feeling of escape, combined with the dizzying knowledge that I now had proof of what had hitherto been mere gossip.

He looked desperate. "I was only joking! Couldn't you tell it was a joke?"

"It wasn't, either! You meant it and you know it!" I felt exhilarated but there was just the slightest touch of horror in my joy.

He rushed past me and fought the door open. At the threshold of freedom, he shot a look back at me. That glance pierced me with a force which made something shrivel inside me. Then the door hissed shut and I was alone.

The dull-sounding slam of the big outer door sent a reverberation through the whole building. As soon as he was gone, a hollow, empty feeling seemed to fill up the inside of my chest.

Dully, I began picking up the pieces of the clarinet which had been scattered on the floor. I bent down to peer under the check-out desk where I thought the mouthpiece might have rolled, kicked aside during our brief struggle. There it was, just within reach. I managed to scoop it toward me and retrieved it. Then I peered closely at it to see if it had been damaged.

Amazingly, it remained unscathed. But upon closer inspection, I saw I was wrong. A tiny hairline fracture could just be made out, almost invisible to the naked eye, but enough, I knew, to alter the pitch of the instrument forever.

* * *

At school the next morning, before homeroom, I looked all over for Jack. Lately, it was getting harder to find him when I needed him. He was spending more time with friends from his other classes. I finally spotted him in the main hallway just outside the principal's office.

"Jack! Wait."

He was walking the other way but waited for me to catch up with him. "What's up?" There was a trace of irritation in his voice.

"Listen, Jack, I gotta talk to you. It's important."

"What's the matter?"

"It's Mark Warren."

"Him? What is it this time?"

"The faggot tried to put the make on me."

"He what?" Jack's face seemed to boil with outraged loathing.

We stared at each other aghast for a moment. Then he said in a quiet, menacing voice: "I'll take care of it."

He knew immediately what to do, and I felt grateful at the bold way he took charge of everything.

Later, as I left math class in second period, I felt a hand tugging my elbow. It was Jack.

"This afternoon. Behind the gym," he whispered cryptically.

"What?"

"Me and the guys are gonna beat the shit out of him."

"I'll be there," I said, my heart beginning to hurry.

"I told you I'd take care of it, didn't I?"

"You sure did."

I watched him walk away down the hall. After that there was no mention of Mark at all. His fate was sealed.

As the afternoon ticked by, I felt myself getting tenser by the minute. Whenever my eyes met Jack's as we passed each other in the hallway between classes, we both looked grim and a little scared of what we knew was going to happen. I purposely kept my eyes averted from the unknowing victim.

Finally the last bell rang. The hallway was filled with students, some laughing, others clowning around. Everyone seemed so carefree. I dawdled by my locker waiting for Jack to come by. Now that the time had come, I felt a little scared. Part of me wished I'd never told Jack about it. But then the knowledge would have eaten away at me until I was consumed by it. Mark Warren was a faggot. How could I not tell?

The hallway started emptying, and still there was no sign of Jack. Had he decided not to do anything about it? Maybe that was for the better. But it was so unlike Jack...

I began to worry. A new thought had come to me: What if it was going to happen without me?

A sense of urgency filled me. Suddenly I knew it was going to happen, with or without me. I had to hurry. Fearing I might miss it, I broke into a run.

Outside, I spotted two or three boys moving purposefully in the direction of the gym. One side of the gym was flush against a steep rise; between it and a set of bleachers facing the playing field was a hidden space where boys often smoked cigarettes and passed magazines back and forth. Already there was a group of boys gathered there, including the tall figure of Jack. Beyond them I saw a pair of flailing arms. As I hurried toward them I caught sight of a smaller boy being pulled around by the collar of his jacket. It was Mark Warren, and his eyes looked scared.

I joined the circle of boys at a tense moment when the action was frozen, as if poised for an explosive burst of energy. Boys stood in a threatening circle around Mark whose arms were caught and pinned back behind him. Then the tableau was set in motion: Mark was dragged back toward the far corner of the little hollow where he was shoved to the ground. The bigger boys gathered in a semicircle around him and he looked up at them with pleading eyes. His lips trembled but he didn't cry.

I felt a jolt as his eyes caught and fastened upon me. There was a shamed look in them and I felt sick now to think of how those same eyes had once gazed upon me with a look of friendship, and how flattered I'd felt then because, despite his small, pursy mouth with its slightly irregular teeth, Mark was quite an attractive boy. But of course that was before I knew about him—before I found out.

Something like bile welled up from my stomach.

"Stand up!" shouted Jack.

Mark had to be pulled to his feet by one of the boys. Trembling, unable to stand on his own, he backed up against the rusty dumpster next to the gym and remained there in a half-crouch. One boy shoved at him—he went tripping and flailing, flying into another boy who propelled him away. He was shoved from one boy to the next like a helpless ping-pong ball.

Suddenly I felt him lunge against me and caught at him to keep myself from stumbling. Then I realized I was hugging the trembling boy to my chest.

"Faggot!" I screamed in a high-pitched voice that sounded like a complete stranger's. It echoed in that empty space, the loudest sound yet. I shoved him away from me, tripping him to the ground. Then, gripped by a blind fury, I began kicking furiously at him. As if this were a pre-arranged signal, the other boys moved in and began pounding on him as he tried to roll away, covering his face. Though he couldn't escape our punishment, not once did he cry out or attempt to fight back. Finally he managed to roll up into a tiny ball with his hands held up to his face. After a few more kicks to his motionless body, we stopped.

Jack spat down on the ground. "Come on, let's get out of here."

He began walking away, calling back over his shoulder: "If you try to tell anyone about this, we'll *really* kick the shit out of you."

We followed him one by one, gloating over what we'd done, our faces calm again after the furious venting of our hatred. (However, once out of sight of our victim, most of the boys broke into a run, laughing and hooting to hide their real fear.) The whole incident had taken place in a few minutes, in an unnatural silence.

Filled with a fascinated loathing, I hung back at the corner of the gym as the last of the boys joined Jack over at the teachers' parking lot. Alone now, one part of me wanting to join the other boys, I watched Mark get slowly and carefully to his feet, brushing himself off. He didn't appear to be as hurt as he'd let on. In fact, it almost seemed as if he was consciously divesting himself of a role he'd temporarily assumed for his own protection. He turned his head and suddenly froze like a startled animal as his eyes met mine...

as if he'd been caught in a very private act. I saw the blood that ran from one nostril, the torn and dirty condition of his jacket and slacks, and wondered how his mom would react when she saw him in that condition. Then I turned and ran to join my companions.

6. Graffiti on the Boys' Room Wall

The old swimming hole still looked the same as ever. Jack and I had come out here, the scene of so many of our childhood games, in a strange mood of nostalgia. It was the spring of our eighth grade; junior high school was almost over for us.

I was surprised when he'd told me he wanted to come out here. Lately, we'd been growing more and more apart; he seemed to prefer the company of older boys, even high school boys, with whom he had more in common. Ever since we'd beaten up Mark, I sensed a distance in Jack's feelings.

Now I tried to revive his interest in some of the games we'd played here; for us, the scrubland had once been transformed into a Wild West full of treacherous enemies, a land where almost anything was likely to happen.

To my disappointment, he didn't seem interested in anything I suggested, peering about and nodding distractedly as if searching for something else to amuse him.

"Hey, come here," he said. Stepping into a clump of bushes on the bank of the gully he nudged at something on the ground with the tip of his shoe.

"Here. Look at this. What do you think it is?" he asked challengingly.

I bent down to examine the object, a shapeless, yellowish discarded something which had become hard and stiff from being out in the sun for so long.

"I don't know. What is it?" I asked. I looked up at him for enlightenment, but suddenly knew from his expression that I shouldn't have asked... that I should have just snickered and pretended to know.

"It's a used rubber. They're all over the place around here. Didn't you ever notice them? I must have seen a million of them out here."

I looked down at it and felt an almost nauseous disgust, as if I'd been confronted with a piece of human stool. Jack prodded it with a stick and snickered. His expression was that of a wicked faun, and a provocative gleam flashed in his eyes as he squatted down in front of me and pulled his wallet out from his back pocket.

"Look here," he said conspiratorially. He fished out a small square packet which he flipped over in his palm and handed to me for inspection.

I examined the cardboard packet. There was a photograph of a handsome young couple frolicking in a sunny, grassy field. I knew immediately what it was.

He took back the packet and worked it open, extracting a plastic-wrapped object. As he tore the wrapping free, I felt a coolness settle in the pit of my stomach.

He held up the condom. It was a circle of translucent pink with a more solid-looking rim of darker pink. Looking at me with an amused confidence, he stuck his thumb in the middle and began slowly unrolling it, showing how snugly it would fit over that for which it was intended. When he was done, his thumb looked as if it were encased in one of those disposable plastic raincoats sold at drugstore counters. He wriggled it around.

I noticed a tiny, cylindrical extension at the tip provided for the ejaculate. Somehow the mundane practicality of it made the condom that much more 'real'.

"Where'd you get them?" I asked as casually as I could.

"From Ron. The high school kids all have them."

He slipped it off his thumb and brought it up to his lips, blowing it up until it swelled into a fat sausage of a balloon, like the balloons of childhood birthday parties. Laughing, he sent it sailing into the air, and I watched as it lazily dropped into the gully.

"Come on, let's go to Hamburger Heaven."

He liked to hang out at this popular burger joint near Freedom High, but I hated it because of all the cigarette smoke which always hung in the air like a thick haze, and the noisy crowds around the video games. But he was convinced that it was *the* place to pick up girls.

When we got there, he stared so boldly and openly at every pretty girl who passed by that some of them began staring back. Most of them were high school girls who seemed so adult to my eyes, but there were also some younger girls from our school whom I recognized.

"A lot of good-looking chicks hang out here, Guy. We should come here more often." His eyes glowed as he appreciatively eyed a long-haired girl sitting at the counter. "Who's she? Do you know her?"

I glanced up. "Oh, that's Debbie Meyers," I answered. "She's in high school. Her brother's in my algebra class."

"Does she have a boyfriend, do you know?"

I shrugged. I noticed Debbie casting occasionally glances our way as if looking at the clock on the wall behind us, but really to ensure that she was still the object of Jack's attention. She was fiddling with the paper wrapper of her straw, twisting it with her fingers into a crooked flat pretzel.

"So what do you think of her? Not bad, eh? She's got tits, anyway."

"Sure does." I examined her breasts without much enthusiasm.

The vulgar way he always talked about girls secretly thrilled me—particularly when he said things like "Look at the size of those jugs" loud enough for them to hear. Most of the girls acted offended, but I suspected some of them really enjoyed the attention. Although he was a relentless chaser of girls, I sometimes believed he secretly despised them—especially those who were considered easy. He called them sleazes and bitches behind their backs and loved to hear the nastiest rumours about them.

The waitress, a slightly plump girl in an orange and white striped uniform, began wiping the tables. Jack kicked my shin under the table and nodded toward her.

"Look at her thighs," he whispered. "They look like sausages. And her ass—it's practically dragging across the floor."

I couldn't help snickering, almost spitting out my mouthful of hot dog. The girl, sensing our teasing, turned around and gave us a dirty look before continuing her work.

"Something tells me she doesn't like us," I said.

"That's no big loss. I wouldn't screw her even if she had a paper bag over her face."

"Come on, let's get out of here."

We went outside and started walking toward the mall. As we were waiting at the intersection for the light to change, Jack spotted some boys across the street.

"Hey, there's Ron and them. Come on, let's go over."

I didn't recognize any of the boys; they all looked old enough to be in high school. I hesitated. "Naw. You go ahead. I'll see you in school tomorrow."

"All right." Though he made a show of disappointment, I sensed he was secretly relieved. He ran across the street to join his friends and I turned for home.

It was true: we were growing apart. He wasn't the Jack I used to play with. Yet my sadness at this loss was being replaced by something quite different.

Jack was undoubtedly the most popular boy in my classes. Because of his interest in girls, he was paying more attention than ever to his personal appearance. While he used to keep his hair cropped short, now he was letting it grow out, parting it to one side so that it hung low on his forehead, almost covering one eye. He had a habit of tossing his head lightly to clear the hair out of his eye, and this mannerism—and the languid, half-conscious motion of his hand to straighten his hair into place—became much imitated among the boys.

He was also growing sideburns which came down almost to the bottoms of his earlobes.

When I'd been his closest friend, I hadn't really noticed how attractive he was. Now I couldn't help but notice how his full lips formed a sensuous natural pout... how long and silky his lashes were... and how piercingly clear his eyes.

He knew, too, that he was the object of much envy. I often saw him standing in front of the boys' room mirror carefully grooming his hair—his already perfect hair—with a longhandled comb. This comb was made of a clear, reddish plastic shot through with streaks of orange, and when he walked down the hall, it stuck jauntily out of his back pocket. Occasionally, when he was bored, he pulled it out right in class and combed his hair, to the shocked admiration of our classmates who snickered in approval. The teachers always chastised him (but only halfheartedly because they, too, were under his spell) and confiscated the comb until the end of class period.

One day I was in the boys' room when I spotted this comb on the ledge above the lavatory sink. Seeing no one about, I slipped it into my jacket pocket. At first I toyed with the idea of returning it with a joke. But as the days passed and I saw him with a new green comb, I decided to keep it. I grew to treasure it, examining it in my bedroom at night, holding it up to the light to make it appear transformed into a fabulous jewel. I turned it over and over in my hands, rubbing it as if it had talismanic powers of evoking its owner. I slept with it by my pillow.

It was almost as if I had a crush on Jack, and I felt a little silly at being prey to such childish emotions.

Our English teacher sometimes asked me to help her grade

tests, and I stayed after school many times to do so. Whenever I corrected Jack's, I always made sure to overlook a certain number of wrong answers. Sometimes I even 'accidentally' misplaced the test sheet and the teacher had to take my word for the score. If Jack was surprised at his unaccountably high test scores, he never showed it. Meanwhile, in my bedroom, a secret cache of Jack's tests and worksheets was growing. Other possessions rapidly joined them: a spiral-bound notebook lost in the student lounge one day; a small rubber ball, confiscated and forgotten in a teacher's desk; a comic book which had been tossed away during lunch hour... all Jack's.

I tried in every possible way to be like Jack. I tried combing my hair the way he did, but it never fell just right. My own hair was wavy and didn't look the same at all. I began dressing as much like him as possible. And one afternoon I spent two long hours searching through all the shops in the mall trying to locate the cologne whose elusive scent I'd detected when we'd chatted in the hallway.

I wanted to *be* Jack.

What bothered me about my feelings toward him was that I knew if he ever learned of them, he would be repulsed and sickened. I had to keep my tortured shame locked inside me, nursing a secret fever I couldn't admit even to my closest friend for fear of the horror it would evoke in him. And the illicit nature of my infatuation only made it burn that much more fiercely, until sometimes I was afraid it would rage out of control.

I envied girls who could openly show their feelings by writing Jack's initials on their notebooks. I knew they often slipped love letters into his locker through the ventilation slats, so I thought of penning a love letter—unsigned, of course—and slipping it in as a prank. But though I wrote dozens of them, I never worked up the courage to take them to school. I was scared to death of being suspected.

In most of our classes the students had assigned seats, usually arranged alphabetically. This meant that I sat behind and to the left of Jack. From that position, I was allowed a view of the back of his head, and his perfect pink ear peeping out from under a neat overhang of hair. Whenever he turned to his neighbor to say something, the open collar of his shirt revealed the smooth tanned column of his neck with just the barest trace of an adam's apple.

I found that I could secretly make him aware of my attention, even from behind. I would stare at the back of his head and concentrate my thoughts until I could sense that he was made distinctively uncomfortable, but without exactly knowing the reason why. He would jerk his shoulder, stare around at the kids behind him in a puzzled manner while I secretly laughed.

Gradually, against my will, my feelings became tinged with erotic overtones. In the boys' room, where I would have shied away before, I found that I could now step up and use the urinal adjacent to the one Jack was using. And in the PE showers, I secretly lived for my glimpses of his muscular back all wet from the water, and the compact firmness of his buttocks. Afterwards in the locker room, when he dried his hair vigorously with a towel, the jiggling dance of his penis was like an impertinent pink tongue being wagged at me.

Wag, wag, wag...

I lay in bed at night going crazy from the memory of such sights, and from the aching desire to feel his hard-muscled arms around me, his chest against mine.

And I turned onto my side and hugged my pillow to my chest, feeling as if some unholy enchantment had cast its spell over me, and (like Sleeping Beauty deep in her death-like sleep of oblivion) only the kiss from the lips of a handsome prince could awaken me... And the pillow became Jack, upon whom I proved my love... and it offered me a temporary salvation, a moment of freedom from the pain of thinking, from the pain of being a boy.

* * *

School was becoming a miserable place for me; I could no longer concentrate in class.

In social studies, Jack always sat in the farthest row over, by the windows. Today he had the wide-awake look of a farm boy—the ideal farm boy of my fantasies. The light from the window illuminated the spray of light brown freckles dotting his nose and cheeks, and the pale peach fuzz shading his high cheekbones, fading into his sideburns. He was wearing a loose, bulky pullover.

His face, which seemed so dreamy at times like this, was lost in reverie. His head was cocked slightly to one side, his mouth pensive and half-open as if in expectation of a kiss. But in his eyes was a certain laughing mockery, the insolent look of a little boy who has pulled a prank that you don't know about yet. At times, without warning, this look would turn sullen, as if you'd just insulted him and he was looking you up and down, trying to decide whether or not to challenge you to a fight.

Mrs. Gomby, the social studies teacher, was speaking, but Jack wasn't taking any notes—he never did. He just leaned back in his seat and listened, his pen poised over his blank notebook, his left hand crooked around in an awkward left-hander's curl.

With his legs crossed, he lounged in his chair with an effortless and unstudied grace as if his presence were a casual but priceless gift bestowed on all his worshipping courtiers.

To my left was a girl named Katrina. As usual, she was sitting in the pose of an attentive note-taker, but her eyes were fixed upon Jack in unabashed worship, gazing at him with a hunger she did nothing to conceal. But Jack paid no attention to her, recrossing his legs and giving his attention to Mrs. Gomby. I could well understand Katrina's dreamy longing, yet the moment *I* let such a desire be known, I would be beaten up.

I shifted about uncomfortably in my chair and tried to return my attention to the teacher, but my mind kept wandering toward Jack. I felt a shivering flutter at the base of my throat as I gazed at him. This boy could move hearts with a tremor of his lips. Underneath his bulky pullover was a body that would make a saint sin.

I swallowed and, against the drone of Mrs. Gomby's talk, tried to mentally strip Jack of his clothing, bit by bit. Surely even the purest, straightest boy must occasionally feel his control slipping when confronted by someone like Jack. I couldn't imagine anyone, boy or girl, looking at him and not desiring him in a sexual way. Such a boy was made to be loved—all the ancient statues and paintings glorified just such beauty.

It was all I could do to keep my feelings secret, and at times the effort was excruciating.

On the surface, I continued to be a model student. But beneath that facade was a monster which no one else knew about, which peeked out at the world through the eyes of a normal-looking boy. No one knew this other Guy Willard, the one who still had certain yearnings he hadn't quite outgrown.

The daydreams were the worst; they kept haunting me... in class... on the bus... at home... in bed. I was made wretched by them, they disgusted me, but I couldn't stop them. They came into my head of their own accord and all I could do was fall under their evil spell.

Jack began biting his nails lightly, and I turned to watch Mrs. Gomby writing on the blackboard. I continued to gaze at the teacher, seemingly listening to her, but actually my mind was far, far away...

I am thinking of how Jack looks in the PE showers, under the spray, his body gleaming with water, turning around and around. His hair is wet and plastered down, and water is dripping into his eyes so he can't see that I'm gazing at him. Suddenly he stops and shakes his hair free. He stares at me. I hadn't realized how engrossed I'd become watching him.

"What are you doing, Willard?"

I stammer out something.

He notices my erection. "You got a boner on. You little faggot."

He turns off the showers and grabs me from behind, locking my shoulders and head in a wrestling hold. Then he yanks me out of the shower room and drags me over to the bench. He calls out: "Hey, Doug, look what I found."

Doug comes running in. When he sees the state I'm in, he laughs. "Caught him with a rod, huh?"

Together they force me down onto the bench until I'm lying supine atop it.

"Cut it out, you guys," I say weakly.

Jack plunks himself down on my chest, his knees digging into my shoulders, his calves pinching my arms against my sides. I am helpless. Down below, Doug sits down harder on my knees.

"What are you guys gonna do to me?" I ask.

"You know we gotta punish you, Guy."

"Listen, it isn't what you think... "

"What else can it be?" Jack looks over his shoulder. "Go ahead, Doug, why doncha give him a hand?"

"Sure."

I feel a hand touch my penis.

"Hey!"

I squirm but it is useless. Nothing I do will dislodge my tormentors. The hand begins stroking me roughly.

"Cut it out! Please!"

"But don't you like it? Isn't it what you wanted to do as you looked at me in the showers back there?"

"No! Don't."

"Don't you like it? Huh?"

I will myself to keep from getting excited, but there is no stopping it. The feel-good increases... steadily. It feels so good, better than anything I've ever done to myself... the weight of his butt on my chest, the look on his face, cruel and gloating... just like the Roman soldier in the movie...

My humiliation cannot be stopped... and he can see the pleasure on my face...

But there's nothing I can do to stop it... it feels too good... it's unstoppable... I don't want it to stop... I'm past the point of no return...

And Jack is looking right into my eyes at the terrible moment of truth, smiling his wicked, wicked smile.

The excitement had made my stomach churn sickeningly... the combination of queasiness and arousal was just too much. There was a buzzing sound in my ears which increased in volume as Mrs. Gomby's voice faded, sounding far away and hollow. The classroom around me turned gray, muffled-looking.

And then, without warning, I threw up.

It happened so suddenly that Mrs. Gomby couldn't disguise the shocked, worried look which transformed her face into that of a matronly grandmother. The kids sitting near me edged away, their desks scraping sharply against the floor. The expressions on their faces plainly showed their disgust. On the desk before me was a steaming mess comprised of bits of carrots, corn, strands of spaghetti thrown up from my insides, the visible manifestation of my inner sickness. I sat with my head down, all wan and wasted, bent over from the secret burden I still carried inside me.

Luckily the bell rang just then. I listened with my eyes closed to the sound of everyone putting away their notebooks and scraping back their chairs. My stomach felt quaky. Mrs. Gomby was standing by my desk asking me if I was all right. I nodded weakly.

As she instructed one of the girls to go for the school nurse, I noticed Jack, with an uncomfortable glance at me, stroll out of the classroom with Katrina right beside him, already talking about something else.

* * *

A few days later I was headed for PE class. With my gym bag slung over my shoulder, I banged into the dressing room to change. I kept my head down, concentrating on changing as quickly and unobtrusively as possible. I ignored the usual rowdy horseplay all around me.

The dank locker room was redolent with the smell of mold and boys' sweat, a combined aroma which was so evocative for me, the very essence of carefree, virile masculinity.

I pulled my t-shirt on and slammed my locker door shut.

As I headed out, I passed right by Jack. He didn't notice me; he was busy talking with Doug as he changed into his gym clothes. Completely nude, he'd just turned to pick out something from his gym bag when he stubbed his toe.

Fearing he'd split a nail, he bent over to examine it closely. That was when I found my gaze rivetted to the sight of his buttock cheeks spread flat, revealing the faint, brownish line marking the cleft... and exposing to the view of the whole world the creasy pink pucker of every boy's most secret spot.

A tiny, beautiful rose.

Quickly I turned away and ran outside.

The boys were lining up in exercise formation, with Coach Kapp explaining the exercises we were going to do today. I found myself unaccountably tensed up. When all the boys had arrived, we began.

Fifty jumping jacks. Fifty knee bends. Thirty sit-ups. Twenty push-ups.

It felt good to move my body; it was like fighting an invisible foe, and the harder I worked out, the more I believed I was defeating him. My muscles were warming up. I could feel the blood coursing through my veins. Sweat dampened my t-shirt.

The push-ups were last. I was pumping away at them so hard that my muscles were aching. Everyone was done, but I pushed myself on—twenty-five, thirty, thirty-five...

Suddenly I sensed Coach Kapp standing by me.

"Guy, don't push yourself too hard. You only have to do twenty." He sounded worried.

After exercises we played a game of touch football. This was the most carefree, fun part of PE. Slamming against each other, swearing, it was a boy's world, millions of miles away from the other classes in school. It was ruled by brute muscular strength, and I felt at one with the others, laughing, kidding, pushing, shoving, forgetting.

After the work-out of the game, we walked wearily back to the gym, a slow, sweat-drenched drag to the showers, where the refreshing stinging spray of warm water awaited us, the wet sound of slapped skin, the engorged biceps, triceps, pectorals...

I pulled my damp t-shirt off and wiped my face with it, breathing in the aroma of my underarm sweat, a sexual scent which secretly thrilled me, for it always evoked this locker room and the undressed boys. I brought my head down like a lonely swan and sniffed...

And finally, the shower. This was the most difficult part. The PE shower room was still a torture chamber for me; the proximity of so much bare flesh from which I had to somehow avert my eyes... Ever since Jack had told me about Mark Warren getting a hard-on in the showers, I had a recurring nightmare of the same thing happening to me.

Mark himself no longer had this problem. I'd heard that he didn't take PE anymore, though it was normally a requirement for graduation. His mother had had him excused for supposed 'health' reasons; he even had a note from his doctor.

Unfortunately, *I* had to be here in the midst of five or six naked boys. I tried desperately to keep my mind on something else as I turned around under the spray of the shower nozzle. My eyes were focussed on the ceiling, the walls, anywhere but upon flesh.

By the time I'd finished, I was among the last to leave. I dressed myself rapidly in the emptying dressing room where the pungent smell of the deodorant used by boys already gone still hovered in the air. A lime-green piece of cloth jammed in the bottom of a locker caught my eye as I was about to dash out. Where had I seen that strange color before? Of course. It was Jack's t-shirt.

I halted.

There was no one in the dressing room now but a couple of boys here early for the next class. They'd never know. I went back to the locker and retrieved the t-shirt as if it were my own. Stuffing it into my gym bag, slinging the bag over my shoulder, I hurried on to my next class. Outside, Jack was nowhere in sight.

That night in my bedroom I clasped the captured t-shirt to my face. I held it to my nose and breathed in the bouquet of male sweat caught in its folds. It was lovely. I slipped off my own shirt and slipped the green one on. This shirt which normally clung to Jack like a second skin now fit me in a loose embrace. I leaned my head back and closed my eyes, feeling an almost dizzying lightheadedness. I thought of how Jack had looked in PE this afternoon—his skin brick red except for the strip of white about his hips, the tiny, curly hairs creeping up the crevice of his butt, peeking shyly from between firm cheeks... the phantom cling of his just-removed jock strap leaving its reddish after-marks, one cutting across his waist and two diagonal ones slashing down his buttocks... the smooth hardness of his cheeks like ripening apples or peaches... and when he bent over, a tiny pink rosebud coming into view...

"Damn you, Jack."

I pictured him stepping into the shower room, his dark nest of curly pubic hair bedizened with jewel-like droplets of water. And the clean pinkness of his dick which I was so scared to look at, so baby soft and flopping... so casually impertinent...

Wag, wag, wag...

I wondered what he was doing now at this very moment—was he going to bed? Or was he already asleep? If so, what was he dreaming about?

"Damn you, Jack, you're making me do this... "

I closed my eyes and let my mind go pleasantly blank.

"Jack... "

Wag, wag, wag...

I opened my eyes to view the sudden white leap, and the archipelago of white islands now dotted out over a lime-green sea...

"Oh, Jack... "

A wave of wretched shame... torturing guilt...

Why? Why had I done it again? Why? Would I ever be free?

* * *

It began so innocently. Sitting in the back of the room in science class while the teacher lectured, I and a girl—Judy, or was it Sonia?—were kissing passionately. As we lipped and tongued each other, the giggles and whispers of the girls sitting around us began to grow louder and louder. Finally it was loud enough to draw the teacher's attention, and Mr. McGuiness, who had been completely unaware of what was going on all this time, rapped his pointer against the blackboard to bring the class to order.

It was then that I pulled away from the kiss and realized with shocked horror that the person I was kissing was not Judy or Sonia, but a boy.

Jack.

And I jerked awake in the middle of the night, trembling, in a cold sweat, gasping.

I lay in bed for a long, long time trying to fall asleep again.

Gradually, I realized I was in another place, a tropical land far away. Was this another dream? I only knew that I'd been picking my way carefully through the midst of some fabulous Grecian ruins, searching for something. The twilight sky was tinged orange and violet. All of a sudden I became aware of a faint movement in the corner of my eye. I turned and saw my quarry slipping away down a flight of wide, shallow steps.

I gave chase, pounding after the other—something or someone—whose face I couldn't get close enough to recognize. All I knew was that I had to catch it. Down torturous twists and turns... past tottering pillars and narrowing walls... into a labyrinthine maze of neatly-trimmed hedges... false passageways and secret doors... down tunnels lit by the smokey glare of torches.

We ended up in a vast, empty stadium whose hugeness seemed to swallow me up. As I raced across its smooth marble floor, the echoes of my footsteps sounded faint and far off. But I somehow knew I was near the end of my chase. My quarry was heading toward a semi-circular amphitheater at the far end. And it was here that I finally cornered it.

Upon the wide, stage-like setting, I waited with trepidation and unmitigated horror for it to turn around and expose its face— a face which some dread premonition in the instant before it turned around told me would be that of a slimy, repulsive monster.

And it was.

And now it was my turn to escape the horror, down twisting alleyways which led through unknown catacombs, my breath coming shorter and shorter until I bolted awake with an agonized groan which still sounded in my blood-thrumming ears even after my eyes were wide open, staring up at my bedroom ceiling.

I sat up and turned the bedside lamp on, then got out of bed and went over to my desk, pulled out the chair and sat down. A glance at the clock told me it was two-thirty in the morning. No one else would be awake at this hour. Slowly I lowered my head onto my hands, resting my throbbing temple on the desk-top.

I thought again of what I'd read in *What Every Boy Should Know*. '...it is quite common for a boy to develop romantic attachments to another of the same sex...' And: 'In most cases, this condition weakens and disappears as one gets older... '

It was all temporary. Of course it was.

But how many other boys were going through this phase? Surely I couldn't be the only one. Lately, there was so much talk about homosexuality in school that it seemed to be the only thing people talked about anymore. In fact, most of the boys seemed fascinated with the topic. Words like 'queer', 'faggot', and 'fairy' had entered all their vocabularies. Other words like 'cocksucker' and 'buttfucker' were so common that they were no longer applied to just queers. Homosexuality was a popular theme for jokes and insults. Some boys (no doubt, so assured of their own heterosexuality that they had nothing to fear) made jokes like: "You better not bend over in the showers if you know what's good for you," rubbing the front of their shorts suggestively. I laughed along with them, secretly wondering how they could be so unconcerned.

Most boys, however, made no secret of the disgust they felt toward fags. I suspected it stemmed from their uncertainty about themselves. Maybe they, too, were 'going through a period of physical changes and curiosity'.

Strangely enough, some of the most outspoken denouncers of homosexuality were those handsome athletes who were no doubt the very type most desired by the tormented fags. I wondered if there was a direct correlation between their good looks and their discomfort with homosexuality.

They never missed an opportunity to jeer at any boy whom they considered less than masculine with their favorite phrase of contempt—even for obviously straight boys—'goddamn faggot'. The very way they pronounced the word 'faggot' left no doubt in anyone's mind that it was the lowest form of insult they could find in their vocabulary: drawing the 'f' sound out like a harsh, punitive sibilant, exploding the rest in a glottal rush, finishing up with their lips twisted into a disdainful sneer. The progressive changes of expression as they said it—from grimace to snarl to sneer—was a visible manifestation of their hatred for the whole tribe.

Accusations of homosexuality were rife, whether they were warranted or not. These accusations ranged from subdued whispers in lowered voices to open taunts and malicious denunciations. In every boys' room, the walls were covered with the inglorious saga of some poor persecuted kid. The amount of graffiti devoted to homosexuals shocked me, and I sensed beneath the ostensible loathing a secret, fascinated interest.

Certain names were repeated so often, and were so ubiquitous, that they gained a notoriety, a celebrity, even. Naturally, Mark Warren's was the most prominent among them. He seemed to bear the brunt of a tremendous amount of hatred—his name was practically a byword throughout the school, appearing on bathroom walls with increasing frequency.

It was like a continuing saga, the way his name travelled through the school. In the boys' room of the language arts building, I'd read: *Mark Warren is a faggot.* In the boys' room next to the study hall was: *M. W. sucks dicks.* But for me, the most fascinating of all was the one in the boys' room of the main admin building: *Mark W. gave me a blow job right here on Feb. 19.* It had a certain earthy reality to it—like journalistic reportage. I thought of my encounter with him in the music room. What if I had been a little too careless (or more brave?) and had let it happen? The very thought of it gave me an ambiguous feeling of horrified wonder.

Ever since that day behind the gym, none of the boys would talk to him. His only friends now were girls. I'd been trying not to think of him, to put him out of my mind, and had succeeded so well that I barely noticed his presence in class. It was as if he didn't exist anymore.

* * *

About a week later, just before the start of PE class, I noticed a group of boys huddled near the foot of the bleachers. They were discussing something furtively in low excited voices. I edged nearer to hear what they were saying.

It seemed they were talking about something that had happened at a Boy Scout camp-out on the previous weekend. From listening to bits of the conversation, a rough picture emerged: In an isolated and hidden grove not far from the tents a certain boy had been held down roughly by a group of stronger boys. Though he'd struggled and whimpered and cried, there was nothing he could do to stop the ruthless procession of boys who each took his turn with him: it was a gang-bang.

"Heinemann went twice."

The boys guffawed.

I looked at them. They'd grown silent and were holding their breaths, their faces pale with excitement, their eyes glowing feverishly. There was a dangerous tension in the air which could swing at any moment toward sudden violence or innocent laughter.

A small boy whose voice hadn't broken yet piped in: "You mean up the ass?"

"Right up the old poop-chute."

The boys broke into laughter and began shoving the smaller boy roughly around, but in a joshing, comradely manner which indicated that he was one of them.

It was at this moment that I finally asked casually as I joined them, "Who was it?"

"Mark Warren."

"The faggot?"

They nodded, looking at me with superior jeering grimaces which twisted their faces into ugly masks. I felt a sudden chill as I tried to hide my shock.

"So that's why he hasn't been in school lately," was all I said.

The coach's whistle pierced the air and we straggled toward the open court and into exercise formation.

7. Teen Confessions

Bobby looked different this year; he had definitely grown much taller and heavier since last summer. He'd been thin back then, even scrawny. Now as he got out of the family van, I noted how much more filled out his chest was. He seemed so self-confident about his new physical maturity that it was I who felt a little bashful at meeting him.

We didn't have much chance to talk during dinner, though our eyes met constantly. It was only after we'd retired to my room where I helped him unpack his clothes that I felt we'd been reunited at last.

My mother joined us soon afterwards, and we helped her set up the camping cot which Bobby always used. We watched her spread crisp clean sheets on it and then unfold a green and black camping blanket she'd pulled out from my closet. As she took one of the pillows from my bed and fluffed it out before putting it on Bobby's cot, she said, "Why don't you boys come down and watch some TV with us? I'll be making popcorn."

I looked at Bobby before replying, "Naw, we have a lot to catch up on."

She smiled. "All right. But be sure and take your showers by ten o'clock. A lot of people will be using the bathroom tonight."

Down below we could hear my little sister and Bobby's two sisters making a racket. As soon as my mother had gone I lay back on my bed and Bobby lay back on the cot.

During our first few moments alone together, I felt an awkwardness which had never been there before. Perhaps it was because I was conscious of what an attractive boy he was turning out to be. I'd never thought of him as good-looking before.

Also, I felt nervous thinking about the games we'd played last summer. They would definitely qualify as 'mutual explorations'... that dreaded phrase which now sounded like an accusation.

But last summer's games seemed to be the farthest thing from his mind. "Wow. Seems like only yesterday I was here. Nothing's changed."

"Yeah."

"You look a lot bigger, Guy."

"I do? You know, I was just thinking the same thing about you." I knew I was getting taller because my mother's friends always told me so, but I never thought of myself as being any bigger than I'd been when junior high was just starting. It didn't seem so long ago. And here it was, already our last summer vacation before high school.

"You know," I said, "I can't believe I'm really going to high school in the fall."

"How do you feel about it?"

"A little scared. I don't know if I'm ready yet. High school always seemed so far off."

"Yeah, I feel the same," he said. "But at the same time, I'm glad to be getting out of junior high. I'm tired of being a kid all the time."

"Really? A part of me still wants to be a kid... "

"You know, this will be the last summer I come here."

"Why's that?" I sat up.

"Once I start high school, I'll probably work part-time to save up money for college. That means I'll be getting a summer job next year."

"Oh." This was news to me. Somehow I'd always assumed that Bobby would show up every summer, and we would compare notes and share secrets before parting again. This time there would be nothing to look forward to when he left. Summer would no longer bring him back to me. He would be growing away from me now.

Suddenly he asked, "What are you thinking about right now, Guy?"

"Why do you always ask that question?" It was true—he often asked it of me, usually at the most uncomfortable times.

"Oh, I don't know. You looked so deep in thought."

"I was just blanking out, I guess. It happens sometimes."

"Are you sad that this is the last summer I'm coming?"

"Damned right. We sure had some good times, didn't we?"

"Yeah."

"Remember that time we snuck down to the living room after midnight just to watch that horror movie on TV?"

"Yeah, and you pretended to fall asleep when the scary part came."

"I was really asleep, I tell you."

"Sure you were... "

And suddenly it was like old times. We challenged each other to see how far back we could remember. As we recalled specific events from our past, I began to realize that Bobby was perhaps the one who understood me better than anyone, despite the fact that the actual time we'd spent together couldn't compare to the time I'd spent with my school friends. We must have been talking for about an hour when Bobby yawned.

"Think it's time we hit the sack?" I said.

"Yeah. It sure was a long drive."

"You wanna take a shower first, or should I?"

"You go ahead."

After we'd both taken our showers and were dressed in pajamas, I said, "Let's trade places this time. You sleep in the bed and I'll take the cot."

"Sounds okay to me."

I turned out the lights and we settled comfortably into our respective beds and lay for a while looking idly up at the ceiling. Before sleeping, I always liked to imagine the whirls and grains in the wood as waves, faces, goblins, eyes... It helped me fall asleep. But tonight I was thinking of last year, and what those goblins and faces probably remembered.

"Guy," said Bobby suddenly in a solemn tone, "I'm kind of worried."

"About what?"

"I think I beat off too much."

"What? Are you serious?" I got up on one elbow to look at him.

"Yes."

"How much is 'too much'?"

"Almost every day. Sometimes twice a day."

"Oh, that's normal for kids our age," I said with some authority.

"Are you sure?"

"Yeah, I read it in a book."

"Well, I'm glad to hear that. I thought I was a sex fiend."

"You're a sex fiend, all right, but not 'cause you beat off." I tried to picture him masturbating, then felt guilty. "Come on," I said. "Let's get to sleep."

I lay back down and turned onto my side facing away from him but was distracted again by his hoarse furtive whisper:

"Hey, Guy, remember the stuff we did last summer? Wasn't

that crazy?"

"Yeah." I held my breath.

"Who could have guessed what we were up to?"

"Come on, go to sleep, will you? I'm trying to fall asleep." But his talk was causing flutters in my stomach, a cool heaviness in my rectum.

"I was just—"

"Listen, I've outgrown all that stuff, okay?" I had a sudden vision of how his erection had looked, and was afraid of what the talk might lead to. "Only fags do that kind of stuff anymore."

"Maybe you're right," he said in a small voice.

"You know what a fag is, don't you?"

"Of course. We have fags at our school, too, you know."

He'd obviously learned a lot since last summer. He'd been so innocent back then—he and I both. I thought of the fun we'd had together, and how ignorant I'd been of the significance of it. Now I knew better. It might have qualified as exploration last year, but not anymore. So many things had happened to me since. I'd learned too much to continue the innocent games we'd played so joyously, so dangerously, and so foolishly...

In the darkness the curtains at the window glowed softly in the moonlight but nothing was distinguishable in the room. My heart felt constricted and I was unable to speak. The silence of the sleeping house filled up the whole universe, punctuated by the ticking of the alarm clock on the bedside table.

My legs felt all weak; if I'd been standing, I might have collapsed. I brought my knees up.

He sighed loudly. The blood was thumping in my ears with a hollow sound. But I would be a good boy. I couldn't afford another slip. I had to wean myself from those 'childish activities which some boys go through—but which they soon outgrow'.

* * *

I must have drifted asleep, for a loud click startled me awake. Actually the sound hadn't been loud at all—but there is a stage between sleep and wakefulness when the slightest noise will give you a jolt.

My first thought was that it was the bedroom door opening. I glanced toward the door but it was shut. Then I remembered Bobby was spending the night with me. Perhaps he'd just stepped out to go to the toilet.

No—I could hear the wooden floorboards creaking softly. Maybe he'd just come back from a trip to the bathroom. What time was it? I couldn't locate the clock immediately. And then I realized I was sleeping on the cot. The clock was over on the bed-side table.

For some reason, Bobby wasn't getting into his bed but was standing somewhere near my cot. What was he doing?

I heard a soft breath, then a stifled cough as if he'd cleared his throat.

And then I felt a sudden startling coolness. He'd lifted the corner of my blanket. Was he planning a prank? I decided to ignore him, pretending to be still asleep.

"Hey, Guy," he whispered.

Or had he? He'd said it so softly that I couldn't tell if he was just clearing his throat.

I tensed up, expecting the thump of a pillow slamming against my head. But instead, a completely unexpected thing happened. The covers came down again, and I felt warmth.

He was in the cot with me. Under the same covers as me.

Was this a joke? I didn't budge and continued feigning sleep, all the while aware of each thump of my heart, the warm press of his body all along my back. He was lying still, and I could feel the soft breaths he took, the rise and fall of his chest. Because the cot had become depressed where we both lay, our two bodies were drawn together.

I could smell the toothpaste he'd used earlier, a different brand from mine.

He didn't seem to be clowning, though. If he were going to do something, he'd have done it already. More likely, he'd gone to the bathroom and forgotten I was in the cot he usually used. He'd slipped in without knowing. That was it.

But then, shouldn't I tell him of his mistake? I'd better do it soon, before he fell asleep again; but maybe he was sleeping already. Why wake him? I was afraid even to budge to check out this fact. I was only aware of the throbbing in my ears, the sweat in my armpits, the churning in my stomach.

How long would this go on? Through my half-opened eyes the ghostly outline of the bedside table gradually became clearer. I could almost make out the clock's face atop it. The faint green glow coming from its numerals were like secret glimmers from another world. My mouth was dry but I was afraid to swallow. My gulp would be loud in the stillness.

Should I jump up and laugh, make a noise, any sound? This joke of his had certainly misfired; it served him right for pulling a stunt like this in the middle of the night. A joke was a joke, but this was carrying things too far. How long had it been going on? It seemed like an eternity of clock-ticking hell. I felt the sweat in my clenched palms.

There was a slight movement. He was backing away from me and getting up again. Had he realized his mistake? Or had he grown tired of the joke, the prank that didn't come off? Or did he believe that I was asleep? I'd been careful to keep my breathing slow and even.

Like a dream he slipped away, and coolness once again returned. I continued my sleeping act. I heard soft footsteps pad back to the bed, the creaking of the springs as he got on, then silence.

Everything had seemed to occur in a trance-like stillness.

The ticking of the clock continued. Now wide awake, I knew I could never get back to sleep, if indeed I'd slept at all. The curtains were backlighted by the soft moonlight. I still didn't dare budge—I was frozen into place, had lost all use of my muscles. I didn't even dare turn over onto my other side. My heart was ratcheting in my chest.

An eternity later, I heard the sound of even breathing from the bed. And even then I didn't move... until a dull, lifeless feeling in my arm under me told me that circulation had long ago ceased to that limb. I rolled onto my back so I could ease it up and free. It felt as if it didn't belong to my body, a heavy, dead weight almost impossible to lift, even with the aid of my other arm. Carefully, I picked it up with my other hand and let it down with a thump. The tingling prickles of itchy pain crept up and down it as circulation returned.

* * *

When I opened my eyes it was morning. I had, after all, fallen asleep. Bobby had apparently already gotten up and opened the curtains, and I could hear him downstairs talking with his sisters. From where I lay on the cot I could see the sky outside, a dream-like shade of turquoise blue devoid of a single cloud.

A vapor trail was being etched on that azure slate by an invisible hand, a sight which inexplicably saddened me with its melancholy evocation of faraway places.

I thought of Bobby last night in the cot with me, snuggled against me. In the light of morning, it was beginning to seem more and more like some weird dream I'd had. I decided to forget about it.

And then suddenly an idea hit me. It seemed so bizarre that I had to digest it for a moment before I could realize its import. I thought with an airy sense of wonder: 'What if Bobby understands everything, and is going through the same changes as me?' The thought was charged with an exciting blend of blasphemy, defilement, anarchy... and release.

When I was a boy there was a children's edition of *Robinson Crusoe* which I loved to flip through. In it was an illustration which had always haunted me. The hero—after years of living alone on an uninhabited island, dressed in rough, tattered garments—is bending down to examine another human's footprint on the sand with a look of open-mouthed bafflement on his face. Now it struck me why I'd always identified so strongly with Crusoe... only my little island was the whole world, making the discovery of a strange footprint in the sand that much more astounding.

It was what I'd always dreamed of, hoped against hope for: finding another boy just like me. But all I felt was a stunned disbelief. Was it possible that Bobby also felt a strange attraction toward other boys? I felt as if I'd discovered my long-lost brother, the soul mate I'd always longed for—a boy to whom I could tell all my secret thoughts, all my guilty deeds.

I wondered if Bobby realized he'd just landed on my private island.

The thing to do now was to find out for sure if he could truly understand my feelings, to get him to admit that he, too, was just like me. What a sense of freedom I would feel, what things we could tell each other... Both of us could open up completely about everything, compare notes...

Somehow, fate had vouchsafed me this last chance to make contact with a real human being, a fellow castaway, on our very last summer vacation together.

I dressed and went down to breakfast.

We spent the morning as if nothing were different. We went to the game arcade at Sunnyside Mall, had hamburgers for lunch, then came back home to watch a baseball game on TV. When it was over, I suggested we go out to the Fort.

There, we idly flipped through comic books and talked of inconsequential things. But all the while I was thinking about what Bobby had done last night, and trying to work up the courage to mention it.

The drone of a single-engined airplane could be heard somewhere high above us, like a persistent mosquito.

"You ever notice," I began, "how jokes which don't come off leave you feeling foolish?"

"Huh? What are you talking about?"

"You know, things like practical jokes. Things you pull on your friends."

"You like to pull practical jokes, Guy?"

"Not like the kind you pull. I don't have the guts."

"I don't get it." He flipped rapidly through the comic book in his hand.

I looked closely at him but he didn't seem to be made uncomfortable by my line of questioning. He didn't seem aware that I was referring to what he'd done last night—if, indeed, he had done anything. I was beginning to doubt it again. Perhaps it had been a dream after all. But I didn't want it to end as a dream.

"Listen, Bobby, can we talk?"

He glanced up, puzzled by the sudden change of tone in my voice. "Sure."

"I mean, seriously talk."

He looked hard at me with just the barest trace of apprehension. Did he guess what I was leading up to?

"Sure," he repeated.

"I was thinking," I said, "that if there were two friends who were close to each other, I mean *very* close, they could say anythng they wanted to each other... even their deepest secrets. And after that, it would be like nothing stood between them. That's the best kind of friendship, I think. Them against the world..."

"What do you mean?" He seemed unconcerned, completely unaware of what my confession was costing me. But I knew that now was the time to make it—there would never be a better opportunity than this.

"Well, sometimes I'll see someone and sort of wonder what he's like—what kinds of things he thinks about and stuff. And I'll really want to become his friend, his best friend. Do you know what I mean?"

He looked puzzled.

I stared down at my own feet, not having the courage to look up. A flush spread over my face and burned my ears.

"You're going to have to promise me that what you're about to hear is just between you and me. Because if you don't, I'm not going to say a thing."

"Why all this seriousness?"

"Because what I'm going to say is something I've never told anyone else."

"Go on."

"Can you understand—" I looked away quickly before continuing. "I don't mean to sound weird or anything, but can you understand how it might be possible for a boy to have certain feelings about another boy?"

"Certain feelings?"

"Yeah." I turned toward him but now it was he who couldn't face me. My throat felt pinched and raw. I swallowed. My bowels were heavy and my palms were wet. Didn't he get my hints? Why didn't he respond? Suddenly I wished I didn't have to be there. But I pressed on:

"I guess from everything I've said so far, you must have figured out... well, let me put it this way. All the time I was growing up, I felt weird, like I was a freak or something, because I started to realize after a while that I was different. When the other boys started getting interested in girls I didn't feel anything. I never did react to girls the way they did, even when I was a little kid. I thought something was wrong, but I didn't want anyone to find out, so I faked it. I pretended to be just like them, 'cause I thought in the back of my mind that I would change when I got older... that I would turn normal... wake up one day and be just like them. In a way I guess I still think so."

His face was beginning to flush.

I gazed at him, silently begging him to be more open with me. He lowered his eyes as he muttered, "But why are you telling me all this?"

"I'm telling you all this 'cause you're my best friend, and I wanted to tell someone who would understand, and I thought you would."

He suddenly raised his face and there was a look of terror on it.

"You're... you're not a homo, are you, Guy? Is that what

you're telling me?"

I felt a pink explosion behind my eyeballs. My breath was suddenly sucked away, leaving me gasping. I had gotten to my feet somehow and my head swam from the drain of blood.

"Tell me it ain't true, Guy."

What he'd done last night—what had it been? Just some silly playing around? Or had I imagined it, dreamed it? Slightly nauseous, I started to move away but felt myself restrained by a strong clasp around my wrist.

"Are you all right, Guy?"

The buzzing in my ears wouldn't go away. From far, far away I could hear the tinkly chimes of the Good Humor Man's ice cream truck, and the children running out to greet him, as if the world hadn't come to a standstill, as if the world hadn't come to an end.

And then I started laughing. I laughed and laughed and couldn't stop.

"What's the matter, Guy?"

"I got you," I said.

"Got me? I don't get it."

"You really believed me, didn't you? Admit it. I really had you going, didn't I?"

A strange look lit up his face.

"You mean— ?"

"I was joking. It was all a joke."

Something in his eyes faded and went out, and then I couldn't read the expression on his face anymore. He looked as if he wanted to laugh, but was unsure whether to be horrified or embarrassed. And I had no idea how I looked to him. Only, I felt as if I'd been dropped from a very great height and was just getting up from my fall, gingerly feeling my bones for any breakage, dusting myself off, and then—to the horrified wonder of the crowd which had gathered around me—walking jauntily away, whistling a merry tune.

SIDE TWO

1. Girls, Girls, Girls

One day, as I was walking in front of a downtown theater where some girls were sitting around, I overheard one of them exclaim softly to her companion (either in admiration or to needle me), "Ooh, sexy butt." When I turned around and caught them gazing at me, they burst into nervous giggles, and one of them prodded her friend. "Don't," she said, "he's cute."

I thought I recognized some girls from my school but I ignored them and continued walking. Still, their tribute had flattered me.

Like many boys, I liked to show off my butt by choosing tight, form-fitting jeans which hugged my body like a second skin. In school, I myself often admired the way certain boys walked, making the seat of their pants dance in a provocative (but thoroughly masculine) manner.

At home I would stand in front of the full-length mirror and admire my own butt, gazing at its smooth, rounded contours, the firm elasticity of its muscles, the enticing vertical cleft between the cheeks, the short transverse fold under each tight buttock.

"Hey, wait up," someone—a girl—called.

I turned around. It was Judy Saunders, a girl I knew slightly. "Me?"

"No, the guy behind you."

I looked around but saw no one.

She laughed. "Yes, you, dum-dum. Mind if I walk home with you?"

"No problem."

She matched her steps to mine and we walked for a while in silence.

"Stuck up," she said playfully. "How come you never talk to me in class?"

I had no answer to this. She was in my US History class at Freedom High, but we'd never gone beyond a casual greeting. It wasn't that I never flirted with girls. I did. But Judy really wasn't my type, and besides, there always seemed to be about two or three boys around her at any given time.

"How come you're so quiet?" she said. "You never say anything in class, either."

"I don't have anything to say."

She giggled. "I know. I hate those people who think they know everything, and hog up the class discussions."

She had both hands thrust into the pockets of her windbreaker. Now she pulled one hand out, and from the pack she was clasping she gingerly extracted a cigarette, halted with her head bent out of the wind to light it with her lighter. Then she re-matched her steps to mine, softly exhaling gray smoke.

"You smoke?" I said, more as a statement than a question.

She looked surprised for a moment, then nodded her head as if she'd just noticed herself in the act. "Yeah. But you don't, do you?"

"No," I answered absentmindedly. I thought with distaste of the designated smoking area behind the school and the smoking lounge where a lot of my friends gathered during lunch hour.

She touched my elbow lightly. "But don't tell anyone I smoke, okay? My mom would kill me if she found out."

"Sure."

"Look at her shoes."

She pointed to a woman walking her dog in the vacant field adjoining a baseball field. The dog was straining at its leash, squealing to be let loose. I saw nothing remarkable in the woman's shoes.

"Stupid shoes, huh?" Judy said.

"Yeah."

"What do you do on weekends?"

"Not much. What is there to do around here?"

"Oh, hang out, I guess. Go to the mall and stuff." She was looking at me expectantly. "There's a dance tonight at school—didn't you know?"

"Yeah, I know—the Green and White dance."

"Do you have a date yet?"

"No."

"Well?" The look of entreaty on her face was so comical that I had to laugh.

"Looks like I've just invited you. Right?"

"Right. You have good taste in women, Guy Willard."

She finished her cigarette, dropped it onto the sidewalk and stubbed it out with her sneaker. "See you at the gym tonight, then."

"What time? Eight o'clock sound good?"

"Great." She gave a cute wave with her hand down by her

waist, then turned and walked across the street.

I really didn't know that much about Judy. Back in junior high school she'd been the butt of some silly gossip for a while. She had been a late bloomer, tall and thin, a little on the gawky side, but that hadn't stopped her from trying out for cheerleader.

Apparently, during the tryouts, as she executed a particularly high jump, the falsies she was wearing had popped right out. It became the talk of the school, and for years afterward, her name was synonymous in my mind with falsies. Since then, though, she'd certainly filled out, and was long past the age when she would need anything to supplement her chest.

At Freedom High, she was still the go-getter: varsity cheerleader, class treasurer, yearbook staff. But she did have a reputation for being a bit pushy. I knew she'd been going steady with a boy named Tyson for a long time. She was one of those girls who never seemed to be without a boyfriend, so obviously she was interested in me as a possible successor to Tyson.

Though she was quite attractive, I didn't feel very comfortable with her. Already, I was looking for an excuse to give if she pressed me for a steady relationship. I'd been going out a lot with a quiet, soft-spoken girl named Wendy, but though we'd talked about going steady, there was really nothing serious between us. I felt free to date any girl I wished.

Recently I found myself much more interested in girls. Like most boys my age, I played the flirting games, the dating games. But unlike them, my interest wasn't sexual. My secret hope was that dating girls would wean me from some of my more unhealthy interests. It was like putting myself through a program of cure: the best way to free my mind of my morbid preoccupations was to have a girlfriend.

Girls were showing much more interest in me, too. There was one girl in my English class named Patti Evans who seemed to have a crush on me. Though she never once tried to talk to me, I would catch her staring at me in class. When I looked up to meet her gaze she always took a second or two longer than necessary to lower her eyes. Even though I had no interest in her, I was always pleased by her attention to me. So I checked daily to make sure she was still casting glances my way. I stole peeks out of the corner of my eye while pretending to take notes and felt reassured when I could satisfy myself that she was still looking at me.

Then one day she didn't look my way once during the entire

class period. I felt as if I'd been snubbed; perhaps she'd found some boyfriend outside of class and had lost her interest in—or hope for—me. I was saddened and hurt, almost insulted by her betrayal.

Ever since I was a little boy, I knew I was one of those whom girls considered cute. I'd discovered that they were charmed by my long lashes... so I'd learned how to lower my eyelids in a certain way to make them look even longer.

From junior high school on, girls had been asking me shyly who I was going with. Even the boys asked me who I was taking to the dances. And now in high school, if a boy didn't have a steady girlfriend, people started wondering about him.

The truth was that I wanted to go steady, but the right girl just hadn't come along yet. I dated girls almost every weekend, without really knowing what I wanted, or what I was after. I just did it because it was the thing to do. And at the same time I felt that if I dated enough girls, someone, somewhere would click for me.

Dutifully I would take someone out to dinner or to a movie and afterwards park the car someplace and make out with her. For me there was always an element of planning involved; I went about it all so methodically. Even as I was kissing her, I would surreptitiously note how much time had passed, and decide whether or not the time was right to make the first tentative fondle of her breasts.

I tried to guess beforehand how far I would be allowed to go with a particular girl. Would I be allowed to undo her bra and caress her breasts—'get some bare tit', as the boys put it? Or would deep kissing be the limit? These games never excited me physically, but I did enjoy the sense of challenge involved.

I never knew whether the girls liked what I was doing, or if they only put up with it for my sake. Sometimes a girl protested and pushed my hand away at the first touch of her breast. But if I left her alone after a rebuff like this, she seemed to think I'd given up too easily—that she really wanted me to try again.

I never went out with any one girl for very long. The most times I asked a girl out for dates was about three, possibly four times. That was how long it took for me to realize that nothing was clicking inside me—that she wasn't the one for me.

However, sometimes the girl would get serious before I was ready. Whenever I sensed this, I'd break it off, even though there were times when I felt almost ready to go steady with her. I always ended up backing off at the last minute with some excuse...because I always had an excuse ready—for myself. I kept looking for little flaws in her looks or her personality, and when I sought them out, they were so easy to find.

So I'd never gotten serious about any girl, though I was beginning to get quite a reputation as a girl-chaser. To my secret dismay, I realized that, unlike most of my friends, I still felt a sense of blankness where girls were concerned. This worried me a lot.

After all, more and more boys *were* becoming serious about girls. Even if they weren't romantically involved, they were obsessed with the desire for sexual conquest. The talk in the locker room after football practice was almost always about which girls would put out and which wouldn't.

I felt left out of all this talk; whenever anyone asked me the dreaded question—"And you, Guy? You getting any pussy lately?"—I learned to bluff a joking answer. At our age virginity was something I wouldn't have dreamed of admitting to. It was a curse which all boys longed to throw off, the loss of which was the most sacred rite of passage of all, the one which forever ended the despised state of childhood. For me, the boys who'd done it were like heroes who'd crossed into a fabled no man's land and returned to tell of it.

* * *

I ate a quick dinner at home, then went upstairs to take a shower. In many ways, this was the most exciting part of the date—the preparation, the anticipation. I felt as if I were preparing my body for combat, donning my armor of masculine beauty.

Now that I was beginning to shave, nothing made me feel manlier than to lather up before the sink with only a bath towel tied around my waist, and to run the razor over my cheeks. Meanwhile, the hot water fogged up the mirror, putting an alluring mist over my reflection. And as I ran my eyes over my shoulders and chest, I could understand why Judy was interested in me.

Since turning sixteen, my body had finally begun to fill out, though it was difficult to tell from day to day. I'd been taking careful weekly note of my height and weight, and knew that I was definitely—and rapidly—gaining in height and weight. I looked forward to stepping on the bathroom scales each night. And the array of tiny pencil slashes creeping up the side of my bedroom door frame was like the measure of my own mounting confidence.

My broadening chest now angled out in a curved line from my tight waist, and my shoulders were filling out too. My buttocks were still small and firm, but my genitals felt heavier in heft. I performed isometric exercises shirtless in front of the bathroom mirror to tone up my muscles... and to admire myself as I shifted into various poses.

I found myself comparing how I stacked up with the other boys. I still envied those who were more developed than me, with broader shoulders and more fleshed-out chests.

From the summer of my sophomore year, I'd begun working out with weights. I'd bought a set of barbells and a book called *The Perfect Body* which explained how to exercise with the barbells. I switched to a diet which provided me with as much protein as possible; my mother began complaining about the number of steaks I consumed. In between meals and after working out, I drank the famous 'stamina drink' recommended by a Swedish body builder I worshipped. It was like a thick milkshake, and consisted of milk, eggs, and honey all whipped together with the blender.

My goal was to have a body like those muscle men I admired so much at the beach every summer. This 'beach' was actually only the shoreline of Echo Lake in the park, but it got quite crowded with sunbathers when the weather was fine. Last summer I'd gone almost every day.

The dark sunglasses I wore gave me the freedom to devour those dream bodies with my eyes. Lying on my stomach pretending to read a book, I scanned those chesty college boys and health club instructors... well-built men whose bikinis waged ever-losing battles to cover up their charms. For me, these men were incarnations of Greek gods, whose solid burnished bodies gleamed like living bronze... whose chests were like hard, flat shields... whose neck, shoulders, arms, and thighs denoted pure power and strength. I could imagine that a finger put to those sinews would feel the steel-like hardness of solid muscle. Their tanned torsos reminded me of the ideal males I'd dreamed of in boyhood as I gazed longingly at the photographs which illustrated the encyclopedia entries on 'Praxelites', 'Michelangelo', and 'Greek Sculpture'.

I stationed myself as close to the water as possible, near a diving board which had been set up temporarily for the summer. Many of the most attractive men liked to go for a swim in the lake, and when they pulled themselves up by the wooden boat dock, the water, as if reluctant to let them go, would tug at them with aqueous fingers, clinging with a last desperate caress. As they stepped up onto land the water streamed off them, leaving their bodies glistening, their hair all wet, their swimsuits clinging so tightly that the outline of their genitals was clearly discernable. Sometimes a bit of pubic hair peeped out from the top of the waistband... and the casual gesture with which the man tugged up his briefs made my heart pound.

Strangely enough, a man's facial looks didn't always matter that much. Although a handsome face was desirable, I lost interest if the man didn't have the body to go with it. What excited me was his aura of masculinity. It was maleness I worshipped. With the concealment provided by my sunglasses, I unashamedly turned my head to gaze after a handsome couple walking by... and everyone assumed, of course, that my admiration was focussed upon the woman.

I still felt that, from a purely aesthetic point of view, women were far less attractive than men—even when judged by the most objective standards. At the beach, because almost everyone wore swimsuits, this was easy to confirm. When the girls walked by (even the most attractive of them), the way their buttocks and thighs jiggled showed the flabby tone of their muscles there. Boys, on the other hand, were more evenly muscled all around. A hand passing over their buttocks and thighs would feel nothing but a satisfying firmness.

*   *   *

We could hear the music from all the way out in the parking lot. As we stepped inside the gym, it was almost deafening. The basketball court had been transformed by some chintzy magic into the scene of Green and White Night. Tables from the cafeteria had been set up against the wall (where the bleachers had been folded in), and streamers in green and white—the school colors—hung from rafters and girders. The smell of popcorn balls and taffy made by girls in the student council or sororities hung over everything. A temporary stage had been set up opposite the home bleachers. The basketball court itself was filled with dancing couples, while here and there the chaperoning teachers looked placidly on.

Judy immediately went off to chat with some friends she'd spotted at a table while I stood there waiting for her. She looked so excited and happy at being here that I didn't take offense.

Above the gym floor, multicolored lights—blue, green, orange—flashed on and off in time to the music, giving the effect of a jerky silent movie to the dancers' movements. I watched the boys and girls jerking about spasmodically, letting their hair fall into their eyes, shuffling their feet, gyrating with puppet-like motions.

In the swirling mass of boys and girls I spotted Jack dancing with a girl named Marybeth. She was energetically pumping her pelvis back and forth, back and forth, with a blank, lost look on her face. No doubt she was unaware that she was so brazenly revealing a very private act, for, to my eyes, her motions were nothing less than a ritualized version of actual sex. The interval between her and Jack was like the blank space between parentheses, a concession to public morality which demarcated the difference between dancing and fucking.

I knew Jack was sexually active because he never lost an opportunity to talk about it afterwards in the locker room. And, true to form, he always seemed to choose the sleaziest, least attractive girls in school—the ones who would put up the least resistance to the one thing he wanted from them.

He himself was beginning to lose his looks. No longer the young god I'd known back in junior high school, he drank too much beer on the weekends, and was getting slightly overweight and flabby. Girls still found him quite attractive, though, and I could see why. His sexual conquests only seemed to add layers of glory to his unshakable macho confidence. There were still times when I felt twinges of my former longing.

Judy finally returned. Grabbing my hand, she pulled me out to the dance floor. As I danced with her, I imagined myself gazing down upon us all. The whole scene had the appearance of an ancient festival orgy performed before some temple dedicated to the gods of heterosexual love. Everyone was lost in his own dance. Alongside the dance floor, others were chatting with their friends, shouting to be heard above the noise of the music.

I felt left out of it all, a stranger from another country who has wandered in to observe the customs of the natives. Was there anyplace here for me? A keen feeling of loneliness pierced me and seemed to spread out of me and float above like a wraith.

Suddenly the lights got dim and the flashing colored lights died away. There was a pause during which the singer took a long drink of Coke, and on-going conversations and laughter came into clear focus. Then the band started playing a slow dance.

Judy pulled me closer to her and put her arms around me. Everywhere around us, couples had collapsed into each other, pressed tightly together. The girls' heads were lolling lazily against the boys' chests or shoulders, and the boys buried their faces in the girls' hair. Arms encircling bodies, hands gripped tightly or loosely behind their partners' backs, the dancers' feet shuffled slowly as they rocked back and forth like seaweed drifting in the tide.

Judy, clasped tightly in my arms, felt like a captive bird. I breathed in the fragrance of her shampoo and felt the soft press of her breasts against me. Her breath wafting softly against my ear was redolent of the spearmint-flavored toothpaste she used. And somewhere I detected the perfume she'd borrowed from her sister tonight—a drop on each earlobe perhaps. But the fresh, spring-like smell which underlay it all was from the acne soap she used, the quintessential smell of a high school girl.

I spotted Jack a few feet away dancing with Marybeth. She looked as if she were being held up on her feet by him. Her face wore the expression of a loose swoon... there was a look of bliss on her upturned face and half-opened lips. Her arms groped up his broad back, her hands buried themselves in his hair. I turned Judy slowly around so I wouldn't have to see it.

The music was now little more than a throbbing of bass and electric organ, the aural equivalent of a pulsing red light. Over that accompaniment, the singer's cat-like vocals whispered a saccharine lyric about disappointment in love, a sentiment completely belied by the sexual throbbing of the music behind her.

Judy and I swayed to the rhythm of the music, bathed in an aura of sweaty boy-girl lusts, our clothes sticking to our skin. There was a low whining in my ears and I felt as if we were aboard a slowly rocking rowboat at the pier, bump-bumping softly against the wooden pylon, the midnight wavelets licking, lapping at the curved hull.

Judy turned her head aside and laid an ear against my chest. She felt so pliable in my arms, her soft flesh molded tightly against my chest and belly. A strand of her hair caught awkwardly between my lips. I freed it by pulling my head away.

The inside of the auditorium was almost completely dark... we were all on a huge barge drifting loose into the night, into the perfumed mystery. There was a certain magic in the moment despite the tawdry reminders of everyday school life all around: desks festooned with colored streamers, the teachers in their suits and dresses, the green-tinted blackboard still bearing traces of the swaths made by a wet cloth which had wiped away algebraic equations. None of it could change my fantasy that we were all on a ship plowing through the night, a passenger liner with festive lights, propelled by desire and memory and dream.

After the band finished their last number, the lights went on and the dance broke up. While the members of the dance committee began cleaning up, and the band were putting away their instruments, Judy and I joined the crowd going out the main entrance, chattering, laughing, to the parking lot out front. Ordinarily it was a teachers' parking lot, but on dance nights it was open to the students.

Outside, couples melted into the darkness, and there were sounds of cars starting up and car doors slamming. Here and there cigarettes were lit up. A girl's voice called out from someplace: "Joanne, your purse!"

I suddenly felt as if something had vanished forever, leaving only the smell of sweat and cheap perfume hanging in the air. A renewed wave of loneliness and self-pity overcame me—because all this was something from which I was forever shut out. At the same time, the moment became tinged with a sense of sadness—sadness, perhaps, at the impending loss of all this. It was almost like nostalgia, or déja vu, but for something which I was experiencing now. And then a strange thought hit me: Was this premature sense of loss what was normally called happiness?

The night was warm, and many people were still standing around talking with friends, reluctant to go home just yet. Judy and I turned our steps toward the darkness of the football field, where we noticed other couples strolling or kissing. The smell of new mown grass and just-turned earth seemed to fill up the moonless night.

As we stepped onto the turf of the playing field, I spotted several couples sneaking off into dark corners of the deserted bleachers. I pointed them out, and Judy whispered, "Let's do the same."

We found a quiet spot just beside the announcer's booth and sat down. She snuggled against me and raised her mouth for a kiss.

I discovered Judy was a passionate kisser; she slipped her tongue into my mouth as soon as our lips met. There was a faint taste of bubble gum. I recalled seeing her in the hallway kissing

110

Tyson just last week. So this was what he was getting then.

She let me suck on her tongue for a while, and then she sucked on mine. I withdrew my tongue from her mouth and we let our lips brush lightly together, then glance away, then come back again for a fleeting touch. When this teasing became too much, we mashed our lips together hard, until we were both straining for breath.

Finally, Judy pulled away. "So tell me: are you still going with Wendy?"

I sat back against the wall of the announcer's booth. "We weren't going steady."

"Oh? Then what's the situation between you? I mean, how serious are you?"

"Well... I don't know."

"What about her? Does she want to go steady?"

"Yeah."

"Do you like her? I mean, a lot?"

I shrugged. "I dunno. Sometimes I like her a lot, and other times I'm not so sure."

"You don't *sound* too serious about her."

"What about you?" I countered. "Aren't you going with someone now?"

"Nope."

"I thought you were going with Tyson."

"Oh we broke up ages ago."

"You still seem pretty friendly."

"Well, we're still friends and everything."

We said nothing for a while. Then she took a pack of cigarettes out of her purse. "Is it okay if I smoke?"

"Sure."

But she made no move to light her cigarette. Across the field, the lights were going out in the gym, section by section.

"Guy? Do you think it's possible to love two people at the same time?"

"I guess so."

She looked at me strangely, in an expectant manner.

I kissed her, not knowing what else to do.

Her hand was resting lightly on my chest as she kissed me, but soon I felt it creep up under my shirt and begin rubbing my chest. I felt uncomfortable because I knew it was a signal for me to reciprocate. I didn't want to touch her, but at the same time, I couldn't tell her to stop.

She pulled away from the kiss and withdrew her hand.

"What's the matter, Guy? I didn't know you were the shy type."

"I'm not."

"Well, what's wrong, then?"

"Nothing's *wrong.*"

"Don't you like what I'm doing?"

I didn't reply.

"What's the matter?" she taunted. "Don't you like girls?"

A chill like an icicle sliced through my heart. I looked at her hard to see if I'd heard right. "What'd you say, Judy?"

"You heard me. What are you gonna do about it?" Her chin was thrusting up at me in a provocative manner.

I got up. "Oh, I like girls all right, Judy, don't worry about that. It's just *you* I don't like."

As I walked down the bleacher aisle and stepped out onto the playing field, I could hear her soft laughter in the darkness behind me, and it sounded so full of bitterness and self-pity that I felt chills run down my spine.

* * *

Walking home, I felt the haunting sense of loneliness I'd experienced earlier at the dance come over me again. It seemed to spread out from some core deep inside me and permeate my whole being. I was thinking of Judy, but my anger at her had diffused and turned into a familiar form of self-loathing.

What was wrong with me? Why couldn't I respond? Was it only a matter of taste? But I'd felt nothing for Judy, no sexual arousal, no romantic interest. Other boys, I was sure, would have gone much further with her, and without the need to tell themselves they were doing it to be like the others.

Jack would have jumped at the chance to fondle Judy; perhaps even now he was with Marybeth, in bed with her. I thought of how Jack would look, naked, then forced my thoughts away from the sight. Did I still feel an unhealthy yearning for him? It seemed like only yesterday that I'd gazed down on him sunbathing... stolen his t-shirt and soiled it. When would I outgrow this childish attitude?

Or was I, after all, turning homosexual?

No. Impossible.

Impossible.

True, viewed from a certain angle, my feelings, actions, thoughts could perhaps be misconstrued by someone who didn't know any better... the muscle magazines I used to collect... the things I'd done with Bobby during summer vacation...the things I fantasized about in class. All that was solid 'evidence' which could implicate me, stamp me as a member of that despised race of beings who walked the face of the earth, normal to all appearances, but who were *not* normal, not real humans. It was terrible how an illusion could be made to seem real by anyone who was maliciously inclined.

But how *was* one elected to membership of that invisible race? And what constituted membership? One act? Two? How many? Did intentions count? Or whether the intent was deliberate or an innocent mistake? Was it too late to change?

Suddenly I felt as if I'd been infected with a dreadful, contagious virus—as if, unknowingly, I'd wandered into a leper colony and discovered only long afterwards that I'd caught the disease from a brief, accidental brush with an inhabitant. And now the dreaded infection was deep inside me, working its way to my heart, weakening my defenses, corrupting me cell by cell.

But of course it was all a mistake, a terrible misunderstanding. Once I sweated out the attack, weathered the fever, I would be all right. Everything would be as it had been.

All I needed was time. I would be falling in love with girls, having sex with them before long. After all, all the boys did. It happened to everyone. I couldn't be an exception. I was normal. Perfectly normal.

It was just a phase I was going through, just as the book had said. A lot of boys went through it, and came out sane and happy on the other side:

Most teens soon grow out of it...
during adolescence, a time of change...
not uncommon for a platonic infatuation for a member of...
even to the point of actual...
not to feel guilt over...
irrepressible...
find themselves doing...
with true maturity comes an understanding of...
at very different rates...
on the average of approximately...

a dull, lethargic feeling of listless...
such as sports or other activities...
twentieth century mores...
prohibited...
changes in attitude...
tell your family doctor about any...
understanding parents...
curiosity, which is quite normal...
mixed-up feelings...
quite normal...
most normal teens soon grow out of it...
most normal teens...
most teens...
Once or twice, or perhaps more, but...

I shut my eyes, but the blackness inside me was much darker than the true night. And for some reason the sidewalk beneath my feet seemed to suck at the soles of my shoes, as if I were walking on top of a gigantic piece of sticky candy.

2. (I Don't Wanna Be) An 'A' Student

The plaza of Sunnyside Mall was crowded, and the soft drink and fast food stands were filled with teenagers. Many of them were sitting around the central fountain under the palm trees.

As I walked up the red brick steps, I could hear music from someone's portable cassette player floating on the breeze.

I was wearing my short-shorts today because it was so warm. I'd purposely chosen my white pair to better set off my tan. Because they were so short, the irritating rub of the center seam was stimulating, and I walked along with the delicious threat of incipient arousal.

I knew my shorts drew people's attention to me, and this was exactly what I wanted. I secretly listened for favorable comments made about me behind my back.

Women in their late twenties and thirties weren't afraid to express their admiration openly, sometimes with whistles. Girls closer to my own age tended to look away quickly whenever I caught their eye, though sometimes they would stare back at me with an almost hurt look in their eyes, as if hopeless of ever winning my interest.

Boys my age, especially the better-looking ones, studiedly ignored me or pretended not to see me, though I knew they did. No doubt they resented any added competition for the girls.

One of the characteristics of beauty is the curious way in which lesser beauty gets 'blotted out' by greater, in proportion to the degree of difference between them. I've often noticed this. For example, in a room full of boys, my attention is naturally attracted to the best-looking one there. If however, an even better-looking boy walks into the room, the first boy's beauty actually seems to fade before my eyes, paling in the light of the more attractive one, and my eyes shift to the new boy, forgetting all about the other.

Thus an attractive boy bristles at the approach of another attractive boy, fearing his own beauty will fade. In high school, I had become particularly sensitive to this instinctive competition for looks. Whenever I entered a room, I quickly spotted the handsomest boy there, then made for a seat at the farthest possible point away from him.

In the plaza the sunlight was dazzling. The heat was so intense that I could feel waves of coolness wafting from the fountain. Teenagers in groups of three and four were sitting along its rim eating ice cream cones and drinking cups of ice-cooled orange juice. Seeing no one I knew, I dawdled along in the shade of the store windows peering into the showrooms.

There were many trendy clothes stores at the mall which catered to teenagers and I made a periodic sweep of them in order to keep abreast of current fashions. Now that I was in high school, I knew how important clothes were. They were an intimate part of a boy's personality, and sometimes made all the difference in how people viewed him. I knew that when someone was confident about his own looks, it was reflected in the way he dressed.

All attractive boys became trendsetters to some extent, whether they wanted to or not. Since they were used to drawing people's eyes, they generally chose their clothes with care, either to bring out their attributes or cover up their drawbacks. Perhaps they even began to feel a certain responsibility to please the watching eyes, to present themselves before the world in the most flattering clothes and hairstyles. The bolder ones among them were usually the first to try something new and daring, and they became the fashion leaders of the school.

These trendsetters knew instinctively who they were; they felt they were born to fulfill this role, as if it were their natural function. Each of them knew he had 'fans' among the student body. A week, maybe two, after he'd started something new, he would find (like a treacherous mirage or double vision) pale imitations of his creations cropping up, reflecting back something he'd once worn, a certain way he'd had of wearing his clothes: leaving several top buttons of his shirt undone; letting a handkerchief hang long and negligently out of a back pocket; wearing old, worn-out belts his father had once worn, leaving the extra length dangling provocatively; wearing a clean length of nautical rope in place of a belt.

To my surprise, I'd discovered that a boy needn't be all that attractive to be a trendsetter. If he possessed a good sense of fashion and dressed with a certain authoritative flair and bravado, he would find the younger boys copying him. Certainly a boy like that was much more desirable than those others who were more attractive by nature, but who dressed like slobs in order to express their so-called rebellion.

I stepped into Blue Genes, which specialized in casual wear. The clerk looked up at my entrance and gave me a nod of recognition.

I went to the racks where the corduroy slacks were, in the hip-hugging style which the television commercials claimed were so sexy. Flipping through them, I picked out a color I liked and made my way to the changing rooms at the back of the store. Even when I didn't have the money to buy anything, I liked to try on new clothes.

There was nothing quite like the delicious private-public feel of slipping into a curtained changing room and stripping off my clothes, with nothing but a single sheet of cloth screening me from the outside world. I liked to get completely nude before the opposing mirrors which duplicated my reflection out into infinity. The sight of so much naked flesh front and back excited me; I loved to savor my own nudity while listening to people chatting just outside the changing room, the clerk talking with another customer, and the announcements being made over the mall's PA system.

I put my shirt on again and tried on the slacks. After appraising them for a while, I stepped outside for the clerk's opinion. This was another pleasure: modelling brand new clothes before someone else's admiring looks.

I suspected this clerk was gay; he liked to tug and pat my clothes into place as he voiced his opinions. Playing innocent, I kept plying him with questions as I felt his hands wander down the backs of my thighs, along my hips, barely listening to his words.

"You look great in them."

"Thanks. But I think I'll look around some more."

"Sure. Take your time." He smiled.

I hurried back to the changing room because I knew he wanted to prolong the conversation. As I slipped out of the slacks, I saw that I was getting aroused.

When I stepped out again, I spotted a teenaged boy coming into the shop.

It was Mark Warren.

He was one of those whose clothes I admired, and perhaps because of this, we'd recently begun to rebuild the tentative friendship broken off so disastrously in junior high school. Mark had made the first overtures in our freshman year of high school, and I'd gradually responded, wondering if he'd forgotten all about the beating Jack and I had given him. For he acted as if it hadn't happened at all. At Freedom High, he was one of the more popular boys, despite the fact that he was something of an outsider.

His reputation, indeed, was a mystery to me. I was almost sure he was homosexual, and most of the people who whispered about him said the same thing. But he had many friends who defended him against this charge, boys as well as girls. My own image of him was permanently associated with the rumor I'd heard about his being gang-banged at Boy Scout camp. This incident had never actually been verified, and was part of the mystery surrounding him. For me, he was cloaked in the enticing garb of depravity reserved for sexual victims; that imagined scene in the abandoned grove was a recurring fantasy for me, with Mark as the helpless object of my brutal lusts. I couldn't help wondering what might have been going through his mind as boy after boy callously assaulted him.

"Hey, Mark," I said cheerfully, "where have you been hiding yourself lately?"

"It's you who's hiding from me. What are you doing today?"

"Nothing. Just hanging around."

In the light of day, that rumor about his rape seemed nothing more than someone's dirty-minded fabrication.

"I'm bored as hell. Listen, would you like to go for a drive?"

I hesitated. "Now?"

"Sure. Unless you don't want to."

I thought of his beautiful red MG convertible, the envy of all the boys at school. I nodded yes.

Mark had changed a lot since junior high. He'd always been different from most of the other boys, of course, being something of a sissy. In high school he still was, though it didn't affect his reputation as much. There were many people who were drawn to him by his resolute individualism.

For many, though, he was still a little difficult to approach. I think they were afraid of his sarcastic wit. His jokes tended to be at the expense of other people. He had the reputation of being just a little bit crazy, the outsider who thumbed his nose at all authority. He frankly said that school was a bore, and despised all the teachers without exception.

His looks and mannerisms were still the kind which outraged most boys our age; the prissy way he walked, the way he waved and fluttered his hands about as he talked. On top of that, he had a habit of carrying around a notebook filled with fashion drawings of dresses and gowns for ladies—fashions of his own design. And the gossip which seemed to flower all around his name only served to add to his mystery—he never confirmed or denied any of it. He knew it made him a sort of legend at school.

His intelligence was also phenomenal, though he was anything but a grind. Without seeming to try at all, he held the highest grade point average in our class. And though most of his friends were girls, there were plenty of boys who sought out his company. Many of them no doubt cultivated his friendship just to get close to the girls who were always around him. Also, his family was somewhat wealthy, and people always enjoyed the parties he gave at his house.

I, too, was making tentative feelers and initiating a cautious friendship. Whenever we ran into each other in the study hall or the student lounge, I stopped to chat with him.

But because to all appearances, he was such an 'obvious' fag, I always made sure when talking to him that my own heterosexuality was never in question. I found myself adopting a faintly mocking, ironic attitude toward him, and making sure we talked only about innocuous things—art or photography—never touching on the topic I most wanted to discuss.

He, too, wanted me to think he was straight, spicing up his conversations with bawdy comments on some of the girls who were his friends. But recently, he was making less and less a pretense of heterosexuality. Though he never came right out and owned up to being gay, he dropped tantalizing hints which teased me and allowed for ambiguous interpretation. It was this tightrope balancing act which made him so interesting.

* * *

I spotted his car in the parking lot immediately. Its canvas top (folded down now) had holes in a couple of places, but in my eyes that only added to its glamour: I loved it. It had a distinctive personality which made it stand out from its drab domestic neighbors.

Mark got into the driver's seat and started up the engine. I vaulted over the passenger door without bothering to open it; the car took off even before I landed, the seat slamming into my back, jolting the breath out of me.

We headed down Fulton Street and turned off onto the curve leading to the interstate. The wind swirling through the open cab made conversation all but impossible except in brief shouts. All I could hear was a hollow roaring in my ears and the throbbing vibrations of the motor. Still, it felt wonderful to cruise like this under the warm sun.

We got on the freeway where the wind made my hair fly around so much I couldn't concentrate on the scenery. Mark pulled straight into the fast lane and put his foot firmly down on the accelerator. We picked up speed.

His driving seemed to reflect some inner compulsion to push himself to the limits. There was indeed something a bit reckless and high voltage in Mark's character, something which skirted the borderline of madness, as if he were deliberately performing a tightwire act before a crowd which was hoping he would slip and fall.

Yet, strangely enough, I didn't feel afraid about his driving. I almost wouldn't have minded dying on the highway in a splendid, flaming car wreck. A shiver ran down my spine as we shot past slower cars. I felt giddy with the drunken exhilaration which comes with high speed.

Mark pointed to the car next to us and shouted something which was lost in the roar of wind. I glanced right and saw nothing unusual, only a middle-aged couple in a late-model family car, the woman staring at us in disbelief. She looked angry and baffled by the sight of us. I nodded back at Mark as if understanding.

He raced the car ahead. The mountains far off to the south looked like woolen blankets thrown casually over a steer's corpse. I turned to look at Mark and saw him squinting against the glare of the sun.

"I gotta put some gas into this thing," he said. "Let's get off the damn freeway."

"Sure."

He pulled over into the slow lane and hit the blinker for the next turn-off.

As we came off the ramp, he down-shifted the engine so suddenly that I was thrown against the dashboard. The smell of exhaust and gasoline accompanied the engine's decrescendo.

At a much slower speed, we drove along McKearny Street, the main thoroughfare of the downtown area. As we approached the large parking lot in front of the bus terminal, I noticed a man standing beside a sheltered bench. He looked at me as we drove by, his head turning to follow our progress.

I glanced quickly at Mark to see his reaction, but he didn't show the least sign of noticing anything out of the ordinary. When he turned to say something to me, however, he caught my look of expectation. For a moment we stared at each other with strange expressions on our faces. Then he gave a short laugh and broke the silence. "You know, sometimes I wonder about those guys."

"What guys?" I had lowered my voice in response to his, though no one could possibly hear us in the car.

"You know... fags."

"What about them?"

"I mean, what can two guys see in each other? It just doesn't make any kind of sense at all, does it?" His face was all innocence.

I felt I was treading on dangerous ground. I detected something false in his voice and was wary about replying immediately. Suddenly I didn't entirely trust him. After all, I had no assurance that he wasn't testing me, trying to catch me in a slip of the tongue, watching for a clue which would give me away. Was I under suspicion? I shrugged. "Don't ask me."

"You know what? One time I was standing at a crosswalk just waiting for the light to turn green so I could cross, when this guy pulls up in his car right in front of me. He was just a regular-looking guy, not a creep or a weirdo or anything. And he rolls down his window and says to me, right there in the middle of the street—in broad daylight—like it was nothing, he says: 'Hey, kid, wanna come home with me and fuck?' Just like that!"

"What'd you do?"

"I told him to go to hell, of course. The lousy faggot."

"Does that kind of thing happen to you a lot, Mark?"

"What do you mean by that?"

I laughed at his look of indignation but he didn't seem to be too put off. He shook his head with a laugh.

"Let's change the subject, Guy."

"Do you think there's a lot of fags?" I pressed, with what I hoped was a casual air.

"Oh, they're all over." He looked at me closely. "Take Mr. Brown, the sophomore English teacher. Wouldn't you say he's one?" There was a delighted gleam in his eyes. This was the kind of juicy gossip he liked to regale me with. Much of it dealt with speculations on who in school was queer and who wasn't. He would

furtively point out someone and say, "He's suspected of being one."
Or: "Him—he's an obvious one, isn't he?"

Now he repeated, "Doesn't Brownie have all the attributes of one?"

I thought of the way Mr. Brown walked, and the fussy way he crossed his legs in class. "I guess so."

"And look at Glen and Mike, the two lovebirds. They're pretty obvious, aren't they?"

"I've always wondered about them." These were a couple of seniors—Glen was president of the student council, and Mike was his inseparable companion. "Are they gay?"

"Oh sure," he said. "They're lovers and don't care who knows it... though they stop short of coming out completely." He savored my look of incredulity before going on: "I think there's a covert understanding between Glen and his parents. After all, he transferred from that exclusive prep school he was in, to Freedom High, just so he could be near Mike."

"How about Mike's parents?"

"He lives alone with his mother. For her, Glen is just a dear friend of her son's. She sees nothing strange about the number of times her son spends the night at Glen's."

I didn't think either Glen or Mike were very attractive. Glen was too large and stocky, with a steely stare peering from behind his dark-rimmed glasses. And Mike with his batting lashes was too effeminate for my taste. Yet I couldn't help feeling a certain jealousy at their exclusive friendship.

"It's amazing that people haven't crucified them for their behavior," I said.

"Oh, when you're as popular as Glen is, then your reputation is pretty secure. Other boys haven't been so lucky."

He went on to tell me about a boy in another school named Kevin who'd emerged from his closet one day with a vengeance. Because it was fashionable among musicians to be bisexual, Kevin, a bass player in a rock band, had let it be known that he was gay. But he'd seriously miscalculated the acceptance of his classmates.

As soon as the word began to spread around, he became the butt of cruel jokes and open derision. His name quickly became a byword via the boys' room walls—people called after him in the hallway, bigger boys picked fights with him. The teachers only made nominal attempts to protect him from the baiting, trying to hide their smiles as the boys—it was always the boys—called him names to his face, right in class. None of his friends rallied to his defense, not even those who'd already suspected his inclinations and had tacitly accepted it (feeling smug about their open-mindedness in doing so.) Closing their eyes to his 'perversions' was one thing—to befriend an avowed homosexual was quite another, and they felt that his brazen declaration was a betrayal of their confidence.

His homosexual friends, according to Mark, felt that their own covers were threatened, and were the most vociferous in denouncing him, abandoning him to his fate. To his credit, however, Kevin never squealed on anyone, for that would have betrayed his own principles. No one knew what his parents' reaction was, but shortly afterwards, he was transferred to another school in another city where his family was not known.

Mark seemed to take a malicious glee in recounting all this...almost as if he felt that the offending homosexual had gotten just deserts for his vice, and that he himself was free of any such taint.

As for me, I told him I felt disgusted with the way Kevin had been treated. "The school should have done something to protect him," I said. "They're always telling us about freedom of expression, but when it comes down to doing something about it, they look the other way."

"What's the matter?" smiled Mark knowingly. "Are you pining away over lost opportunities?"

"Get lost!" I said, flushing.

"You know, you just might be the type a gay boy would fall for."

I hated the expression on his face just then, a look which combined amusement, derision, and a hint of curious questioning.

He laughed at my embarrassment. I wondered if he derived a sadistic pleasure from these games of his, coyly enticing me with illicit possibilities, but leaving a safety net so that if I ever made a move, he could always rear up, act offended, and leave me ignobly exposed. But then I myself sometimes teased him with ambiguous hints, knowing fully well I could never risk my reputation with anything more than that.

"There's a gas station," he said.

As he pulled into a self-service station, he suddenly seemed to be filled up with nervous tension of some kind; his knees were pumping up and down.

"Watch this," he said as we stopped at a pump. He reached into the glove compartment and pulled out a pair of old-fashioned sunglasses. As he slipped them on, he altered his face into a puzzled, blankly open-mouthed expression, as if listening intently for something. And I realized that I'd just witnessed his instant transformation into a blind person.

"Give me a hand, will you?" he muttered to me in an undertone.

He groped for my arm. I immediately fell in with the charade, leaping out my side of the car and opening the door for him. Staring straight ahead, he cautiously felt his way out of the driver's seat. The way he pulled off his act with such audacity gave me a giddy feeling of excitement.

I unscrewed the gas cap as he reached out for the nozzle of the gas pump. Because he supposedly couldn't see what he was doing, he shot some gas all over the side of the car before I could safely guide the nozzle into the hole. The stench of the gas stung my nostrils, but it was all I could do to keep from laughing.

The other drivers, along with the attendant, were staring in sympathy, not yet realizing the unlikelihood of a blind person putting gas into a car, but responding to an instinctive concern for handicapped people. Perhaps they thought I was training him or something. If they suspected anything, it must have been allayed by Mark's convincing performance. The attendant came over.

"How much do I owe you?" asked Mark, with the slightest hint of an English accent.

The attendant read the price on the meter, one hand winding the meter back to zero. "$4.75, sir."

Mark cupped a hand behind his ear. "Excuse me?"

The attendant raised his voice. "$4.75."

Mark fished into his pocket and pulled out a handful of rumpled bills and coins, poured them cascading into the attendant's hurriedly outstretched palm. The attendant diligently counted out the right amount and carefully, one hand touching Mark's other hand in signal, put it back into the palm.

Mark stuffed the change into his pocket, and with my assistance, found his way back to the driver's seat.

"Thank you, my good man," he said to me.

I shut the door, skipped around the front and hopped into the passenger seat. Mark started the car up with a roar and we squealed out of there, leaving rubber skid marks all over the pavement. I could only imagine the open-mouthed disbelief of the poor duped attendant.

As soon as we were in the clear, we laughed at the top of our voices.

"How'd you think up a prank like that?" I asked.

He just smirked.

"You're crazy, Mark, you really are."

"Thank you, my good man. I take that as a high compliment."

He stamped his foot down heavily on the accelerator and I felt myself pulled back into the seat as we shot straight ahead into an intersection whose traffic light had just turned yellow.

3. Class Flirt

After Judy, it was another girl. Events outside my control, it seemed, were conspiring to push me and Vanessa Hunter together. I'd known for quite some time that she was interested in me. Before class she always asked me about the homework assignment or the reading... and after class walked with me to my next class. And all during class she stared at me. When our eyes met she smiled awkwardly and glanced quickly down at her notes and then just as quickly looked up again to see if I was still looking.

She was very pretty, one of the more attractive girls in the junior class. She had a unique half-skipping stride which made her breasts bounce under her sweater when she walked. And she was constantly aware of all those boys' eyes on her, for she was always getting in trouble with the teachers for violating the school dress code. One time she'd been sent home for wearing a loose-knit sweater with no bra underneath. She was the type of girl that the boys loved and the girls hated... Yet despite her reputation as a flirt, she wasn't one of those girls whom we joked about in the locker room. She seemed more mature than most other girls, and a little distant. Her beauty put her in a class of her own.

There was something about her that scared me a little; she was such a free spirit that I felt intimidated. And there might have been a part of me that was jealous of the way she drew people's attention. In any case, she was around me so much in school that many people thought we were already going steady.

I was putting my books away just after saying goodbye to her when someone slammed into me from behind, sending me crashing into my locker. I whirled around, fists clenched, ready for a fight. But it was only Jack.

He feinted some punches at me which went whishing past my ears—a little too close for comfort.

"Hey Willard, I saw you talking with Vanessa Hunter just now."

"Oh? What about her? She's always talking with me."

"I know. That's why I'm pissed off."

Though he was joking, I sensed a very real anger beneath the banter. Vanessa had told me that Jack had asked her out several times, but she'd always refused.

He was still one of the more popular boys in school, but lately I'd lost my awe of him. Perhaps it was because I'd grown physically bigger since those far-off junior high days when I'd idolized him. In fact, we were now the same height, and thanks to my weightlifting, I even had a better build.

And the girls seemed more attracted to me. Jack was definitely a guy's guy, interested mainly in sports and cars, while I was able to talk about music, art, and other topics which girls found more enjoyable.

"Come on, Jack, I'm not interested in her. She's not my type."

"Well it sure seems like you're *her* type."

"We're just friends, that's all."

"Just friends, my ass. I wish she'd be friends with me. She don't even wanna talk with me."

I looked into his eyes and saw the real hurt there. Despite all the girlfriends he'd had, he seemed to have fallen hard for Vanessa. And perhaps for the first time in his life, the object of his desire was not a sleaze; he knew now how it felt to fall in love with someone who cared nothing for him. Perhaps because of this, he often disparaged Vanessa in front of the other guys. I could tell it was his envy of me now which had put him in an almost belligerent mood.

"Jack, I'm not interested in her, period."

"Not interested in her?" He gave me a disbelieving look. "Guy, you don't know what you're saying."

"What's so great about her? I mean, she's nice and everything, but you make it sound like she's a goddess. I don't think she's *that* great."

"Shit." He pulled out his wallet and showed me a photograph. It had apparently been taken at the beach last summer with a telephoto lens; Vanessa was lying back on a beach towel wearing her famous string bikini.

"Where'd you get this?" I asked.

"I bought it from Fred Gale." Fred Gale was one of the school yearbook's photographers, a boy who always walked around with a camera slung around his neck. It was rumored that he would sell pictures of girls undressing in their bedrooms—for a hefty price.

I had a sudden image of Jack lying on his bed gazing at this picture, and it depressed me. Vanessa was a cut above his usual girlfriends, and his obsessive yearning for her was probably putting her more out of his reach. I handed back the photo.

As he slipped it into his wallet, he peered around furtively before leaning in to whisper in my ear: "She puts out. I know it for a fact."

"Who told you?"

"Ron Holmes."

Ron was the big sports hero of Freedom High, idolized by the teachers, adored by the girls, and the envy of all the boys. He was everything a boy could wish to be: handsome, statuesque, friendly and outgoing. And he had an almost magical charisma. Though still only a junior, he was perhaps the most popular boy in school. As for girlfriends, he had his pick of the lot. There wasn't a girl who would willingly turn him down. Every two weeks he had a different girl on his arm. The thought that Vanessa might have slept with him gave me a strange thrill. I tried to hide my excitement. "Ron's always bragging," I said. "I don't know how far to believe him anymore."

Ron wasn't the only one who bragged about his conquests—a lot of boys did. The talk in the locker rooms recently was getting raunchier and raunchier. Boys who'd had sex with girls made no secret of it. And talking about it later in the locker room was like a ritual, a rite of passage which sanctified the act and gave it status. It almost seemed that boys did it just so they could tell the others about it, cementing their macho camaraderie. A sexual conquest was the ultimate badge of masculinity, and the guys who'd scored formed a select group. I was feeling more and more left out of their circle.

Jack was looking right at me.

"She's an easy lay. You'll have no trouble scoring with her." It certainly was true that Vanessa had made her willingness quite evident to me, yet I was bothered by Jack's taunting.

"I don't know about that." I began moving the books around in my locker.

"Why not?" he insisted. "What's the matter? You know she likes you, right? She'll give it to you if you press hard enough. Girls like to play hard to get. It's part of their act."

It was almost as if he himself stood to gain from my conquest of Vanessa. I knew in my heart he wanted it so much more than me that I was tempted to say: "Go ahead. You can have her. I don't want her." But instead I said, "Come on, I can handle my own love life."

"Hey, listen," he said. "When you take her out next time, promise me one thing. Promise me you'll try to get into her pants."

"All right, I will. But remember," I smiled, "I'm only doing it for you."

"Get outta here." He punched my arm.

As I walked away, he called to my back in a mocking voice, "Guy, if you can't fuck her, there's something wrong with you."

I whirled around and stared at him. The mad glint in his eye—which could only be envy—was like a challenge to me. A challenge from which I couldn't back down anymore. A challenge I couldn't keep putting off indefinitely.

At noon I spotted Vanessa in the lunch room and went over to her table. She was sitting with a couple of girlfriends, but as if it had been pre-arranged, the other two girls got up and left after a brief greeting.

She said to me with a serious face, "I thought you were trying to avoid me."

"Avoid you? Why? What makes you say that?"

"Well, from the way you've been acting. I thought—well, I don't know."

I toyed with my milk straw for a moment, then leaned down and sucked up a cool stab of milk from the half-pint carton. She was smiling when I looked up.

I noticed several places on her cheeks and chin where the pimples had been skillfully covered up with make-up. Her skin had an unnatural sheen to it, caused by the skin-tightening effects of her acne soap. Her eyebrows had been plucked recently, and she wore a purplish shade of lipstick. The edges of her hair where it brushed against her cheeks were dyed silver.

"Are you mad at me?" I said.

"No. Not really."

"I sure wish I could figure you out."

"Why don't you try?"

"Okay, I will." I looked at her. "How about going out with me tonight?"

She lazily twirled a lock of her hair around and around a finger. "Well, I had some other plans, but since it's you who's asking..."

"Come on, Vanessa, will you go out with me?" I saw her eyes shift in intensity.

"Um, sure." Calmly she lifted her milk, jabbed the straw

absentmindedly between her lips several times before looking down, guiding it in. As she sucked up the milk, her eyes were on mine, big and shining.

Later that afternoon, when I stepped into the boys' room, a bit of graffiti above the urinal caught my eye. Someone had scrawled roughly in pencil: 'Vanessa Fucks'.

I had a strong suspicion it was Jack's doing.

* * *

We watched a movie at a downtown theater. I was unable to concentrate on the screen at all—my head was so filled with what was coming up later. I'd determined to have sex with Vanessa tonight at any cost. The time had come for me to join the ranks of the experienced boys.

My stomach was all knotted up at the approach of the test, for, inevitably, it had taken the form of a challenge which I had to face up to, a call to combat. I had to do it in order to be accepted by the guys.

I felt the sweat in my palms.

The end of the movie came almost without my noticing it. We walked out to my car in the theater parking lot. Vanessa skipped around to the passenger side as I slid into the driver's seat and unlocked the door for her.

As soon as she sat down, she punched in a dance station on the radio and immediately the synthesized thumps of the bass, the ticks of the drum machine filled the car. Re-arranging the rear-view mirror so she could see herself in it, she flicked her hair back several times, then fussed with her make-up.

I started up the engine and joined the line of cars nosing out of the parking lot. "So... where do we go next?"

She looked at me. "Someplace where we can be, you know, alone."

"And where might that be?"

"Well, there's no one at my house right now."

As I stared at her in the dark interior of the car, her face was suddenly illuminated by a passing headlight.

"Sure."

As I drove, she slipped her hand into mine. The moon was off to our right, just nudging over the mountains. Vanessa gazed at it for a while in silence, then pulled out a pack of cigarettes from her coat pocket and lit one up, blowing the smoke out with a long exhalation.

She lived at the far northern end of town, in a sprawling old wooden two-storey house approached by a long dirt driveway. In the moonlight I noted its peeling paint and rusting rain-gutters. Attached to the whole back side of the house was a long, screened-in veranda.

My car bounced around as it hit the potholes hidden in the road. I slowed down and drove forward at a crawl until I found an open space where I could park. I shut the engine off and the radio sounded unbelievably loud in the silence. I turned it off.

The house looked dark and unlived-in.

"Like I said, there's no one home," she said. "Come on, let's go in."

We got out and walked to the veranda. Opening the door, she turned on the light.

There was a comfortable clutter inside. In one corner was an unused washing machine with a hand-cranked wringer. Leaning against it were half a dozen fold-up lawn chairs. An assorted pile of Christmas tree ornaments and colored lights was in one cardboard box. Another box was filled with yellowing paperbacks—Westerns, murder mysteries, and science fiction.

As I gazed about, Vanessa walked over to a small stereo and turned on the radio; it was already tuned to the dance station we'd been listening to in the car. Then she dimmed the light she'd just turned on and led me by the hand to a low collapsible sofa in one corner.

"I like to sit here at night and watch the moon sometimes," she said. "Why don't you sit here next to me?"

"All right." I sank down onto its soft cushions and gazed out the screened window. The moon was not visible from here, though I could see its pale light shimmering on the leaves of the trees in the yard.

"Brrr, I'm cold," she said suddenly, hugging herself. She took my arm, pulled it behind her and snuggled back into it. "There." She looked at me impishly. "Isn't that so much better?"

"Yes."

She leaned in for a kiss. Her soft lips shivered into mine with little nips and caresses. Soon her tongue was brazenly probing inside my mouth with experienced curls and rolls. Where had she gained such mastery, such expertise? I suddenly envisioned all the other boys she must have kissed, in movie theaters, in the backseats of cars, on baby-sitting couches. How many had there been? I tried to picture this army of predecessors and suddenly felt as if I could taste all those other boys' mouths.

Her muffled moans made tiny vibrations within my own mouth, almost as if I myself were moaning. She came up for air and pulled slowly away. A long string of saliva stretched between our mouths, lengthening like spun glass as she pulled farther back. It glistened in the dark for a moment before she reached a hand up and plucked it away with a finger. She giggled.

"You're a good kisser, Guy."

"Not compared to you."

"We girls are made for kissing."

It was true; girls seemed to be born with the ability to kiss. I remembered my first kiss back in junior high school, and even then the girl, Denise, knew all the tricks: how to tease, to lull, to inflame... Where did they all learn it?

Suddenly she reached up and ruffled my hair.

"Hey!"

"You look cuter with your hair straight back instead of hanging down over your forehead."

"I don't care."

"Wait. I just want to test your reflexes. Here." She held up her index finger. "All right, now follow my finger with your eyes. Look left... look right... look up... look—"

When I looked down, she snagged my nose with her finger. She giggled. I grabbed her arm and pinned her back against the couch by her wrists. She squirmed about, straining against her blouse, then after a brief struggle, flopped back, exhausted, breathing fast and laughing, red in the face.

"Say 'uncle'," I commanded.

"Okay, okay, 'uncle'."

I let her go very cautiously, still alert for a sneak attack. But she seemed to have vented all her energy already. She rubbed her wrists.

"Ow. You really hurt me, dummy. I didn't think you'd take it so seriously."

She straightened her hair which had come undone, then paused, looking at me.

"How come you're not like the other boys, Guy?"

I felt my heart grow faint. "What do you mean?"

132

"Well, you're... different."

"Different? In what way?"

"Well, you're—you seem more mature. I don't know how to explain it so well."

"Try. I wanna know."

Without saying a word she took my hand and placed it on her breast. "Most guys like to do this."

"Well, so do I. But I like to work up to it in stages."

"And after that? How many stages do you work up to?"

"I guess that all depends on how far you'll let me go."

"And if I don't let you know?"

"Well, I just might go until there's nowhere else to go."

"Then I guess that's about where I want to go."

"All the way?" I said teasingly.

And when she didn't reply, I knew she meant it. A feeling of queasiness welled up in my stomach.

She pinched the front of her blouse with her fingers and flapped it back and forth a little. "Boy, am I hot." She gave a short giggle, and then a goofy look came over her face as she reached for the top button of her blouse. "Mind if I take off a button or two?"

"Sure, be my guest."

"Tell me when to stop," she said, looking up coyly from her downward-turned lashes. Suddenly I felt caught up in forces beyond me, powerless, for I realized that this was what her games were leading up to. She was in control now—and probably always had been.

With a hint of taunting in her eyes, she looked directly at me as if saying, "Well? Aren't you man enough to stop me? Stop me if you can. If you dare, that is." Or was it the look of collusion in a game we were both playing out? I didn't know. I couldn't understand this girl who seemed so much more experienced than me.

I helplessly watched her loosen one button, and then another... and yet another until all the buttons were undone. Looking at me a little guiltily, she slipped out of her blouse. She was wearing a French-cut bra with lacy fringes.

"I didn't hear you say 'stop' yet, so here goes nothing." She reached awkwardly back with both hands and undid the clasp in back, then pulled away her bra.

It was the first time I'd seen a girl's breasts, outside of magazine photos. Other girls had let me touch them under their sweaters, but no one had so boldly exposed herself like this. She leaned back a little and looked aside, allowing me to gaze at them. I noticed tiny goose-bumps all over the surface of the skin, especially around the nipples, while faint bluish veins criss-crossed on the underside of each breast. The nipples were tensed erect, and looked pinched and shrivelled up.

Suddenly shy under my scrutiny, she abruptly put her hands over her breasts.

I had to do something. I reached out and pulled her hands off, then fondled a breast, marvelling at its elasticity. She submitted to this exploration in silence. Indeed, her silence told me I was in charge now. I lightly pinched a nipple between my thumb and middle finger. It felt like the rubber eraser on the head of a pencil. In response, she reached out toward me and rubbed her palm over my chest. I still had my shirt on.

Afraid to break the silence, I began unbuttoning my shirt, my fingers shaking slightly.

I caught a whiff of my own sweat, and it had a tart, unfamiliar tang.

She sank back down against the cushions and arched her back. It was a clear invitation. I'd secretly been dreading this moment, wishing time would slow down and give me an excuse to postpone it.

Putting my shirt aside, I lowered myself slowly on top of her, and when our upper bodies met, hers shrank slightly at the contact. I heard her sharp indrawn breath, and then her lips were on mine. She shivered beneath me as we kissed.

Her skin was warm, and her lips were also heating up. I suddenly recalled Jack telling me long ago: "When their lips get hot, that means they're hot down there." Indeed, there was a smell in this room identical to that smell I'd noticed when Jack was kissing Sheri on that long-ago day.

Suddenly Vanessa pulled away from the kiss, almost in petulance, and shook the hair out of her eyes. I pushed myself away from her. I had sweated slightly and my damp chest had stuck to hers. She picked at a lash, then rubbed her eyes. Then turning onto her side, she undid her jeans and wriggled out of them. She was down to her panties, and as she lay on her side her breasts drooped down sideways, their nipples framed by pale white triangles in the shape of last summer's bikini tops. The soft whispery vocals of a female singer crooned on the radio.

Vanessa reached out a hand. I felt her palm brush my chest,

then her finger began drawing lazy loops on it, running lightly over a nipple. Then the finger worked slowly downward in intricate filigrees toward my stomach and then toyed along the waist of my jeans.

Without pausing to think, I undid the snap and the zipper. But once my jeans were off, I hesitated to get completely naked; I sat there in my briefs.

Her hand returned to the elastic waistband of my briefs. Then it lightly brushed over my genitals.

"What's the matter, Guy?"

"I'm—I guess I'm just nervous."

"You're shivering."

Her fingers returned to the soft lump under my briefs.

"I guess you don't like me that much, Guy."

"I do like you, Vanessa. You know I do."

"I guess it's me, then."

"You know it's not."

Hoping to distract her, or to excite myself, I reached down to her panties. Hiding my nervousness, and with a vague feeling of revulsion, I began working them off. She complied wordlessly, lifting her hips to aid me. I slipped them smoothly off of her, then dropped them down onto the floor.

She lay back awaiting my next move.

The faint stink which I'd been vaguely aware of for some time now became much stronger. It was not the smell of sweat so much as a shrimpy, fishy odor. I had a vision of an underwater grotto slick with kelp.

She brought her knee up as if to ward off my curious inspection—or it might have been a reflex prompted by her nervousness. I slowly pulled her knee down and pushed her thighs apart, gazing down as they opened for me.

It was then that I felt, with a dreadful, sinking sense of inevitability, a premonition that everything was useless.

For there I saw, fringed with a sparse, wispy beard, the wet, half-open lips of a village idiot. Between those lips, like glinting drool, clung slimy streaks of a melted-cheese-like substance, giving it a gluey, crustacean look. I thought of a slick, bloated oyster clinging to a slimy, seaweedy rock.

This was what all the boys dreamed of. *This* was what they were after. *This* was what tortured them at night, got them hard in the morning, kept them restless all through the school-day.

I felt sickened, and knew with a sense of crushing finality that I could never go through with it tonight—maybe never in my life. This was *not* what I was after.

I was almost jolted by the touch of her hand on me again. She was pulling my briefs down, and I let her. I knew I wasn't the first boy she was seeing naked, and my limpness made me feel wretched.

Through half-closed eyes I watched as she pushed her hair out of her eyes and began caressing me awkwardly. But her touches were too delicate—she had no idea how a boy liked to be touched.

The fear of failure which had been flitting through me all evening now became overwhelming. Try as I might, I could get nothing, not an iota of feeling into me. As I'd secretly suspected all along, I was destined to fail where others succeeded. Would she tell the other girls? And then would it get around to all the boys?

There was a helpless look on her face. Or was she embarrassed, ashamed? I was unable to read that expression. Her face was a shadow in the gloom.

Feeling disgusted with myself, I reached down to touch her. Bracing myself, I slipped a finger into the clammy crevice, wormed it in, and buried it in the damp warmth. I heard her sigh. Keeping my face averted, I began to thrust my finger in and out, glancing up occasionally at her trance-like concentration.

I wanted to go home. As my finger groped within her, I held my breath as a strong, salty smell welled up from someplace. For as long as I could, I continued to thrust my finger in and out. Her thighs had flattened out, involuntarily it seemed, to accommodate me.

I was wondering what I was doing here. Did I have to go through all this to prove myself to the other boys?

Jack should be doing this. Or Ron. Or any other boy.

I stopped moving my finger and pulled it out. I was wondering what excuse I could give for not going through with it tonight. Did such things happen? And then, all of a sudden, I heard a tiny rasping sound.

Peering closely, I realized it wasn't what I'd thought it was at first. It was coming from the other place.

Vanessa put her hand down to cover herself. "Oh God, this is embarrassing." She turned onto her side, facing away from me. "Oh God."

I felt bewildered, foolish, trapped. "What—?"

"The air gets inside."

She curled up petulantly into a fetal position. Then she reached her hand down to pick up her clothes and began dressing without another word.

"Vanessa. Wait."

She made no reply, only savagely thrusting her legs into her jeans, whipping on her blouse without bothering to put her bra on.

"I'm sorry, Vanessa, I—"

"No," she said. "It's all my fault. I knew from the start you didn't want to. I shouldn't have even tried—"

"Come on, listen—"

"Just leave me alone, okay? Just forget this ever happened."

"Listen, Vanessa—"

She turned her savage pout away from me. I touched her gently but she shrugged away my touch.

"Will you just go home now, please?"

I gazed at her back for a while longer, then began dressing.

* * *

As I drove home, I thought of how exhilarated I should have been: I'd gotten off without having to disgrace myself by attempting something I couldn't do. I was lucky to have escaped a more traumatic failure. And my secret was safe because Vanessa would never dare reveal her own embarrassment.

Yet my relief was tinged with a profound self-disgust which I was unable to shake. I wondered if I would have to spend the rest of my life feigning an interest in women just to be like the others, hiding my true disgust at what all other men found so exciting.

Suddenly I felt nauseous and pulled over to the curb. I realized I was on a side street by Horizon Park. I shut off the engine and stepped out.

The night sky above was like a midnight-blue transparency laid over the bottomless spangling of the stars. As I stepped to the corner, the darkness suddenly turned a ghastly green, then with audible clicks yellow, then red. The traffic lights were directing nonexistent traffic.

I turned right at the corner, my shadow spun three ways by different light sources. From here, the sidewalk curved away from the street's edge into the thick darkness of the park. I followed this as if into a pocket.

As I stepped into the darkness under the trees, I thought of the slimy slug-like thing that all boys were supposed to love. At this moment, a girl's pussy seemed to me the ugliest thing in the world. Why did it have to be so slimy-looking and mollusky, so rancid and dripping with gooey passion... If only it looked a little more agreeable, I might not have had any problems.

But of course, the problem was with me. Vanessa was just a normal girl with normal passions, and she was made like any other girl. I was one of the few boys who wasn't excited by what was between her legs: a damp hole, perfectly shaped to receive what every boy was dying to put into it.

It wasn't fair. It just wasn't fair.

Suddenly a flashlight was shining in my face, blinding me. Shielding my eyes, I made out the silhouette of a policeman detaching himself from the darkness. A cop—the ultimate symbol of law and order in our society...

I felt a stab of panic—as if my thoughts had been monitored.

"Hold it right there, son. Where are you going?"

"I'm just taking a walk," I muttered, shielding my face, my privacy, my human dignity from the eyeball-stabbing light.

"Do you have any ID on you?"

"Why? What did I do?"

"Listen, kid, I don't want any backtalk. Just get your ID. *Now.*"

I reached into my back pocket, staggered by the authority and power in that voice. I handed over my driver's license. The light flashed down upon the license in his hand, then up to my face again.

"What are you doing in the park alone at night?"

I felt as if I'd stumbled onto a movie set... this just didn't happen in real life. As far as I knew there was no law against walking alone in the park at night. What was this, an elaborate prank?

"I'm coming home from my girlfriend's house."

"Girlfriend, huh. Girlfriend. Did you hear that, Trent?" he asked sneeringly, over his shoulder.

There was a snort from the shadows to the left. So there were more of them. I was scared now. That tone of disbelief and contempt... could police read people's minds now?

"According to this, you live at 421 Maple. Do you still live there?"

"Yeah... uh, yes sir."

"That's the other way if I remember correctly."

"I know. I—"

"Here." He handed back the driver's license. "Go on home. And don't get lost this time."

I pocketed my wallet and glanced at him. At this moment, that look of contempt in his small piggy eyes revealed for me the brutal animal nature instinctive to the whole human race.

I turned and walked back to my car. On this spring night the whole world seemed to be coming apart, society's fabric ripping at the seams, its stitches popping off with an ugly farting sound.

* * *

I saw Jack in the hallway between classes the next day and walked up quietly behind him. He was busy at his locker and hadn't noticed my approach. Before he knew what was up I gripped him by the neck and tried to bring him down to his knees but he twisted out of my hold.

"Hey, what's up?" he asked, shoving me back playfully. He was chewing gum.

"Well," I said. "Guess what?"

"What?"

I smiled.

"What?" he repeated.

"I went out with Vanessa last night."

"And?"

I just continued to smile. And then, as he realized the implications of my gloating expression, he looked as if he'd just been punched in the stomach. "You mean you—"

I nodded with a conspiratorial grin. I expected him to pound me on the back with glee after all the encouragement he'd given me, but he merely turned away without a word. A little disappointed at his lack of enthusiasm, I casually passed my finger under his nose a couple of times.

"Well?" I taunted.

"What's that all about?"

"I haven't washed that finger since last night."

His eyes got big and he grabbed me by the wrist and yanked my finger forcefully up to his nose again. With an intent look on his face and a manic glint in his eyes, he sniffed hard at it. It was comic in a way, but at the same time, pathetic... I felt as if I'd stabbed him or crushed something forever inside him. I tried to shake myself loose.

"You lucky bastard," he said. He didn't let go of my hand, though.

There was a faraway look on his face. I tried to pull my hand away again but he still wouldn't let go. When he spoke next, his voice was barely above a whisper; in the softest tones I'd ever heard him utter, he said:

"You lucky bastard. You lucky, lucky bastard..."

4. Technically a Virgin

It was summer again and I was sunbathing at Echo Lake in my bikini, a skimpy blue pair which was the merest wisp of cloth, a kiss away from nudity. There was a lazy, relaxed feeling all along the shore, with the scent of sandalwood floating in the air, mixed with the tang of marijuana. Families had brought picnic lunches, and teenagers were tossing frisbees back and forth.

I uncapped my coconut-scented suntan lotion and sniffed it before squeezing some into my palm and rubbing it onto my skin in smooth, sensual motions. Sunbathers here made no secret of the way they loved to caress their own bodies.

When my whole body was glistening from the lotion, I lay back on my towel and let my mind drift in a silver haze of bliss. As the sun slowly warmed me up, I became almost totally mindless, as if all my senses were concentrated and limited to the surface of my skin.

The sun was my secret lover and I let my body be teased and licked by him. The drowsiness which gradually overcame me resembled the euphoria of a sexy daydream, or the lazy anticipation of a summer afternoon's masturbation.

I knew I was pulling the fawning glances of both men and girls toward me like a magnet. It flattered me to know that their eyes were on me, even as I lay on my towel with my eyes shut. Sometimes, just to make sure they were watching, I blinked my eyes open, or peered furtively through my lashes to ensure that at least one of the watchers was still there, and the verification was like a soothing relief.

The people who frequented the lakeside in summer could be divided roughly into two groups: the watchers and the watched. And the relationship between them was symbiotic. The young, attractive boys and girls who basked so narcissistically in the bright sunshine were actually dependent upon their counterparts to achieve their fullest pleasure; the knowledge that we represented the unattainable dream ideal for someone gave a sort of legitimacy to our preening, made of it almost an art.

My audience was the older men who'd come out for a bit of sun with their families, and the young girls who were dreaming of finding a boyfriend here. I learned little tricks with which to court their looks, for I grew to need their glances. Each admiring look was like a long-distance kiss whose caress I felt on my skin where it fell.

Sometimes I actually became sexually aroused, and lay there with a hard-on under my bikini, my forearm pressed against my eyes not only to shield the sun, but to let the voyeurs have their eyeful without fear of their gaze being interrupted.

I never felt guilty about my narcissism because I knew that any young person who had an attractive body liked to show it off. It was natural. That was why activities like skinnydipping were so popular.

These parties where boys and girls swim together in the nude had become a sort of fad at Freedom High. Last week, two friends named Al and Tom had invited me, along with three girls from another school. We'd gone to a secluded riverbank far out in the country.

The girls hadn't seemed shy at all about taking their clothes off in front of us. Though there was a casualness about the whole situation, I sensed that it was an act, a pose to emphasize the extent of our daring, for a certain tension lurked in the very way our glances never went below waist-level. It became increasingly obvious that, even as we talked of other things and clowned around, we all took an intense interest in each other's bodies.

But we weren't allowed to let this interest show. It was important to maintain a sense of decorum, to be cool. When the tension became too unbearable for Al, he lost it by getting hard, and the girls shrieked with laughter. Tom and I dowsed his passion by splashing cold water on it, while Al himself looked shamefaced and contrite at his inability to maintain.

I imagined now how a voyeur with a pair of binoculars would have seen us. Al didn't have such a bad body, though Tom was a little too thin to be considered attractive. I was definitely the best-looking one there. I pictured the voyeur focussing his binoculars on me, my skin tanned the deep brown of a deliciously exotic island boy with a saucy white anti-tan hugging my hips like a phantom bikini.

"Hi, Guy. How's it going?"

I opened my eyes and saw Mark Warren standing over me. I sat up.

He was shading his eyes as he sat down next to me, squinting to keep out the glare of the sun. "You here all alone?"

"Yeah." I generally liked to come to the lake by myself. Whenever I came with a friend, I quickly grew irritated at the way he openly and embarrassingly admired the pretty girls there, pointing with his finger and commenting aloud. Besides, I found I drew more looks from girls (and men) when I sunbathed alone.

"I hear you broke up with Vanessa."

"We were never going together."

"Oh. Well, my friends and I were wondering if you'd care to join us."

"Friends?"

He pointed over to a spot where I saw three girls. One of them waved.

"I don't know..."

"You don't find them to your taste?"

"It's not that."

"That's all right. I'm trying to shake them anyway." He leaned closer. "Listen. I just got a shipment of something good at home, but there's not enough to go around for the whole group. What do you say to just you and me going to my house and trying it out? I won't tell the others."

"Just me and you?"

"Sure. The two of us. Alone." A tension had crept into his voice and I automatically went on my guard. He sensed my uneasiness; I heard him ask with the barest hint of insinuation: "What's the matter? Scared?"

I stared at the sarcastic smile on his face. "Why should I be scared?"

"Maybe because you think I'm one of these." He dangled his wrist weakly and made a gesture as if he were pawing the air.

"Cut it out," I said, looking around. "You know I don't like those kinds of jokes."

"I was just kidding. Can't you take a little joke?"

"With you, I never know whether you're serious or not."

"Okay, then I'm seriously asking you now: would you like to come or not?"

"All right. Just give me a chance to change into my clothes."

His glance flicked down at my bikini. "Why? I like you the way you are."

"Knock it off, will you?"

I was glad I hadn't gotten hard.

* * *

In his room Mark had an elaborate roll-top desk which he said his father had bought him in Singapore. Now he opened the bottom drawer of it and pulled out a sandwich bag filled with a green leafy-looking substance. He held it up to his cheek.

"Wanna try some of this?" he asked.

I knew right away what it was, but tried not to let my excitement show. There was nothing more uncool in our school than someone who hadn't smoked pot before.

"Sure."

He pulled out a record album and poured a small pile of the marijuana onto it, then pinched some between his thumb and middle finger, crushing it up. With his other hand he slipped out a rolling paper from a pack of them, and began skillfully rolling a joint. The facility with which he did it showed that he'd had quite a bit of practice.

He held out the rolled joint toward me. "Go ahead. Take the first hit."

He flicked his lighter on and I put the joint into my mouth, leaned down toward the flame. I took a deep drag as I knew I was supposed to do; a harshness filled my throat and I coughed.

He grinned. "First time?"

"No. It's just been so long since I've had some that I have to get used to it again. That's all."

He didn't say anything, though I knew he must have seen through my lie. I was grateful to him for not exposing me.

"Good stuff," I said.

I handed it back to him and he took a deep hit. As he held in his breath, a little smoke leaked from his nostrils.

He returned it to me and I took another hit. We passed the joint back and forth for a little while. I didn't know what to expect, and tried to act as much at my ease as possible. All I could feel was a slight headache beginning to spread from my temples.

There was something inherently seductive in the act of smoking a joint with a friend... the way we kept our voices down as if engaged in a secret mission... sucking on the same joint passed from hand to hand... the world outside seemed a thousand miles away.

Suddenly he looked straight at me and giggled. I giggled along with him, though I found nothing funny.

"You like it, huh?" he said.

"Love it."

A delicious giddiness was slowly spreading through me. I felt a beatific satisfaction with the world at large... with the armchair I was sitting in, with the greenish way the sky in the west was tinged, with the achingly beautiful way the wispy clouds were etched. They seemed to be tensed for the coming sunset... for the orange ball of the sun to pierce them with radiance.

The window of Mark's bedroom faced a park across the street, and beyond it a residential hillside. The park's sprinkler system had come on and the air was filled with a fine spray shooting out from invisible sprayers. Iridescent rainbow fragments hovered like wraiths over the bright green carpet of grass.

We finished the joint and Mark got up and walked to the window to look outside. I leaned back in the chair gazing lazily at him.

He was wearing a red and white striped t-shirt and low-slung hip-huggers, or yachting pants, which came down to mid-shin. He stood for a long time looking out the window, almost as if deliberately giving me time to admire the firm plumpness of his buttocks. His pants were so tight that I could see he had no underwear on underneath. I quickly shifted my eyes away when he turned around.

A crystalline clear thought emerged from the myriad images swirling in my mind: this boy is almost certainly gay. In the silence I listened to the chug-chugging sound of the sprinklers in the park as they turned like tiny robot sentinels beneath the hissing spray.

Suddenly, as if guessing my thoughts, Mark said: "Hey, Guy, what do you think that faggot Mr. Brown said to me the other day?"

"Don't call him that."

"Why not? Because that's exactly what he is."

"There's no proof of that."

"Oh no? Not even when he walks like this?"

He put his hand on his hip and did a passable imitation of the teacher's walk, taking pert little steps which made his buttocks wiggle seductively. Then he sat down on the edge of the bed, delicately crossing his legs one over the other, girl-style, before folding his hands and settling them on his knee.

I laughed, although a part of me felt distinctly uncomfortable. Whenever boys told fag jokes, I always felt a twinge of shame and angry helplessness. In some inexplicable way, I felt that such talk was a secret stab at me, even when it was obviously gossip about someone else.

"Come on, Mark, cut it out. Brownie's not a bad guy. He gave me an 'A' in English last year."

"Yeah, because he thinks you're cute."

"Cut it out." I felt a little guilty because it was true: I'd courted the teacher's favors by staying after class and talking with him, knowing he probably fancied me.

"Hey Guy, do you know how you can tell queers from normal guys?"

"No, how?"

"The second knuckles on their fingers are hairy. Hah! Caught you looking!"

He was right: I had instinctively checked my knuckles without thinking. At his laughter I burned with shame, somehow feeling guilty.

"Oh, come on. It's only a joke." He seemed surprised at how embarrassed I was, and no doubt that brought out his cruel streak—he loved to see people squirm under his barbs. He eagerly pursued the topic: "Here's another joke. Do you know the motto of the Greek army?"

"No, what's the motto of the Greek army?"

"'Never leave your buddies behind.' Get it? 'Never leave your buddy's behind.'"

"I get it, I get it." I couldn't help laughing along with him, much as I wished he'd change the subject.

"Tell me," he went on, "what did one queer say to the other?"

"What?"

"'Let's get one thing straight between us.' Get it? One thing—straight." He wrapped his palm around an imaginary penis.

I let out an exasperated groan.

He leaned his head back laughed throatily, in a warm tenor which sent a shiver down my spine.

"Come on," I said, to change the topic, "let's smoke some more."

"All right."

Outside, the sky had faded to an empty silver color, and in its heartless vastness, a few gem-like pinpricks were sprinkled, the evening's first stars.

We sat in the growing dark looking out the window at the sky. A soft opalescent glow of lights came from beyond the trees in the park. I raised myself up on my elbows and saw the lights in the houses opposite like a string of jewels against a background of dark velvet.

* * *

The second joint didn't taste so harsh. In fact, I became aware of a seductive sweetness which seemed to pierce through to the deepest part of me. I felt grateful to Mark for inviting me here and introducing me to the joys of this drug.

We finished the second joint, and Mark lay back on his bed.

"Do you feel better, Guy?" he asked, lying there gazing up at the ceiling.

"Much better. Thanks to your medication."

"You've been so unsociable recently. I guess it must have really hurt you to break up with Vanessa, huh?"

"I told you I was never really going steady with her."

He looked at me. "Oh? Then you might be interested to hear that I saw her with Ron Holmes yesterday. They looked quite chummy."

"So?" Despite my casual reply, I was surprised at the stab of hurt his statement gave me.

"You're not jealous?"

"Not at all. In fact, Ron's welcome to her."

"Ron Holmes is welcome to any girl in school."

"That's true."

He lowered his voice. "Listen, I happen to have some dirt on Ronnie that might change your image of him." There was a wicked glint in his eyes.

"Oh?" A thrill went through me; I could tell he had some juicy gossip coming up. Though I didn't know how far to believe him sometimes, he always told his stories so well that I found myself captivated.

"You might not believe this, but..."

As his tale unfolded, I found myself becoming fascinated by it, though only halfbelieving it.

According to Mark, Ron's happy facade hid a tormented Don Juan who was a slave to an almost pathological desire to have sex with as many girls as possible. Cursed with a monstrous libido over which he had almost no control, he was sometimes driven— in order to add spice and variety to his endless, monotonous quest—to pluck fruit of a more exotic kind.

147

There was never a shortage of boys, mostly heterosexual, who would do anything for him for a glance, a word, a smile of approval. They felt happy in the presence of his magical charm as if some of his popularity might rub off onto them. To be seen talking with him between classes—even for one minute—was to have people eagerly ask the lucky conversee what the subject of their talk had been.

And Ron didn't mind dispensing his glory to the least of his worshipful devotees, even freshmen, who were only too willing for some excuse to get close to him. If, for instance, he hadn't been able to date a girl for several days due to a heavy practice schedule, or was forbidden by the coach to have sex before a big game, the boys understood that, for him, it was like being deprived of an essential ingredient of life such as air or water, and they understood completely when he complained that girls were such blabbermouths who liked to kiss and tell; and that boys, unlike girls, could be trusted to keep a secret between pals, and that, really, if you closed your eyes, you couldn't tell the difference...

It was amazing how many boys fell for this line and stooped to do his bidding. But who wouldn't? One look into his sparkling blue eyes, at his dazzling smile, his blond locks, a wisp of which curled rebelliously down over his forehead... he was irresistible. Mark said he knew of 'a certain boy' who'd fallen for it.

One day 'the boy' had been sitting on the bleachers after school watching Ron at baseball practice. To his thrilled surprise, as 'the boy' was walking home, Ron pulled over in his car and offered him a ride home. Naturally he accepted.

But instead of driving him straight home, Ron turned into the park and made a detour out toward the duck pond which was usually deserted during the week. 'The boy' saw nothing strange in this. On the contrary he rejoiced, for it allowed him to be with his hero that much longer.

He didn't ask questions.

They parked under the willow trees whose tendril-like branches brushed the hood and top of the car, enclosing them in a gauzy, pale green curtain. And they began talking in confidential tones.

'The boy' didn't need much prodding, for he'd been secretly head over heels in love with Ron ever since he first saw him on opening day assembly. He pretended to reluctantly acquiesce to Ron's urgings and pleas, when in fact he could barely restrain himself from such an unexpected feast.

The sports hero let his seat back all the way until he was stretched out as if on a dentist's seat. From that position, he allowed 'the boy' to go to work on him, and 'the boy' worked his heart out. In fact, 'the boy' was torn between a desire to use every loving trick he knew, and the fear of being exposed for what he was. He ended up by play-acting the part of an inexperienced boy who unwittingly gives his partner the most exquisite pleasure.

When he was done, Ron zipped up, returned his seat to the upright position and asked, "Where do you wanna be let off?" as he backed the car out.

Not a word was mentioned about what had just taken place, not a single comment. It was as if it hadn't happened, or that it was a brief, business-like transaction which required no further attention. 'The boy' felt let down and hurt, and his initial euphoria gave way to a grim and bitter satisfaction at the thought of all the other people in school who had suffered the same crushing humiliation.

"Did you see him since then?" I asked.

"See who since when?"

"You know... Ron. I'm sure that if you told him your feelings—"

"Oh, get lost! I'm not 'the boy'."

I laughed. "Oh yeah, that's right. I keep for*get*ting."

"Do you want me to introduce you to 'the boy'? Maybe you'd like to get a few pointers on how to please a guy."

"Forget it! That's not in my line."

"Oh? Don't knock it till you've tried it."

"Why? Have *you* tried it?"

"Of course not." He smirked. "But even if I did, do you think I'd tell *you*?"

"Sure. We're friends, aren't we?"

"Not *that* close friends..."

He had been rolling a third joint during the telling of the story, and now he lit it up.

It was completely dark outside now, and as I gazed past Mark's face at the night sky framed by the window, I saw a sudden flash in the sky.

"Look," I said, "a shooting star."

"Where?"

He turned to look, but it was long gone. The meteor's quick

slide down the sky had occurred in the blink of an eye, like the striking of a celestial match, snuffed out almost before I'd had a chance to register my own reactions.

He turned back to me. "Can I ask you a personal question, Guy?"

"Sure."

"All those girlfriends you had—Wendy, Judy, Vanessa...how do you do it? I mean, you seem to have no trouble getting girls."

"You have plenty of girls around you, too."

"Those are just friends, not girlfriends. It's different."

"How so?"

"Well, you don't think I'm actually fucking them, do you?"

"I don't know—"

"I don't even have to *ask* if you fucked Judy or Vanessa. I just assume you do."

The statement made me feel good. In high school it was virtually an insult to call another boy a virgin, so my tacit acknowledgement of his statement had been automatic. But I was keenly conscious of the falsity of my claim. Something inside me made me want to turn my guilt against him, to make him an accomplice in my lying.

"You mean to tell me you're still a virgin, Mark?"

"I didn't say that." He took a deep drag at the joint and handed it to me. "I lost it when I was thirteen," he said somewhat smugly.

"Thirteen?" At that age, I had just discovered masturbation, and considered myself all-knowing merely because some other boys hadn't. Mark had already been experienced then. I felt crushed. And then I thought about it. If he wasn't a virgin, and all the girls around him were just 'friends'... I saw how to belittle his new-found superiority, to bring him down to my level.

"Was it with a boy or a girl?" I asked with a smirk.

"Does it matter?"

I felt a jolt. My taunt hadn't fazed him at all. In fact he seemed to take it in stride. This was the first time he hadn't directly denied my innuendoes about his sexual leaning.

His face, when he turned to look at me, wore the strangest expression, an enigmatic mask which I despaired of ever reading. Was it a mocking grin, or just a gentle smile?

"Are you feeling all right, Guy? You look a little sick."

"It... it must be from all our smoking."

He was staring at me now, and I grew uncomfortable. I had

to turn away from his gaze. A sudden thought popped into my head.

"Mark, can I ask you a question?"

"Sure."

"The stories about you... at that Boy Scout campout back in junior high school. Are they true?"

"Stories?" He looked away. "Oh, them." He slid off the bed and sat down on the floor. For a long time he was silent, picking at his toe. I noted the tiny hairs at the nape of his neck, just below the cleanly barbered hair, and for some reason found this sight so erotic that I felt faint. My eyes misted over and I felt a lightheadedness distance me from the bedroom. I brought my knees up to my chin to hide the sudden erection which blossomed hot in my jeans. I'd never felt such an instantaneous excitement, so powerful that it hurt.

"Well?" I prodded.

"They say I was gang-banged, don't they?"

I nodded, not trusting my voice to speak.

"It wasn't exactly a gang-bang. But I was caught."

"Doing what?"

"You know. With Jeff Lyons, a guy from another school." He took a hit and exhaled quickly. "A couple of the guys that caught us made me take turns with them, with the promise that they wouldn't tell on us."

A heavy weight settled in the pit of my stomach. I knew I was about to ask a question which would change my whole life.

"Mark. Are you gay?"

He looked at me but said nothing. The heaviness in my stomach wouldn't lift. Finally he said:

"Would it change anything if I said I was?"

"I—don't know."

He looked down at his toes. "You've probably guessed anyway, so I'll go ahead and say it. Yes. I'm gay. I like boys and I always have."

I felt as if I'd just exhaled, though I knew I was still holding my breath. "But do you like girls, too? I mean, if you see a good-looking girl, do you feel anything?"

"Of course. I had a crush on a girl named Leona for a whole year. It's just that my first experience was with a boy, and that's probably what made me the way I am. If my first experience had been with a girl, who knows what might have happened?"

"So when you told me just now that you lost your virginity at thirteen, it was with a boy?"

"Actually, I lost my virginity when I was twelve, in the sixth grade. But that sounds too young for most people to believe."

The memory of the time I'd bullied Mark in the music room came back to me. So it had been true then, all the things I'd accused him of. He had done those things with boys, he had already been experienced. Yet, even after hearing this confession from his own lips, I still found it hard to truly believe in. Such things just didn't happen to someone you actually knew.

"Who was it?" I asked, my voice almost a croak.

"A friend of mine named Dave."

"Dave who? Do I know him?"

"No. This was in summer camp. He's from Oregon."

"Have you ever done it with a girl?"

"No."

"But if you had your choice—let's say you were marooned on a desert island and could pick one other person to be with you. Which would you choose, a boy or a girl?"

"I don't know. That's hard to say. Like I told you, I've never been with a girl yet, so I don't know what it's like. If it turns out I like it better, sure, I'll turn hetero for the rest of my life."

And then he looked questioningly at me.

"How about *you*? Did you ever think about doing it with boys?"

My throat felt raw. "Sometimes. But only things like beating off together... things everyone does. Heck, my cousin Bobby and I used to beat off together when we were kids. But we never thought of doing—anything else."

"'Anything else'...?" he prompted me with a catch in his throat. "What is 'anything else'?"

I flushed. My head was throbbing, and I felt almost suffocated... my ears felt stopped up.

"You know," I said with a parched mouth, "blow jobs and that kind of stuff."

The sound of a passing car sliced sharply into my consciousness after what seemed a long moment of complete silence, as if the whole universe had halted a moment at my words. These were words I'd never dreamed of saying to another boy. But I knew if I stopped now I would regret it forever.

"Mark... have you ever... sucked a guy off?"

152

He laughed, then leaned forward onto his elbows and slid his legs out from underneath so that he was lying flat upon his stomach. In an attitude of reverie, he rested his cheek upon a fist, bending one knee coquettishly so that his heel lazily brushed a buttock. The position only emphasized the rounded fullness of his buttocks and I was disconcerted. I hugged my knees harder against my chest.

"Like I said, my first experience was with Dave. And that was one of the things we did."

"You actually did it to him?" I asked.

He shrugged. "I guess I always wondered what it would be like, so the best way to find out was to do it."

"What was it... like?"

"You mean the first time?"

"Yeah. Weren't you scared?"

"Not at the time. But I was scared that someone might find out about it later."

"What was it like?" I prompted again.

"You mean, how did it feel? Oh, about like what you might expect: hot and hard. As for the taste, it was a little salty."

"Gross!" I felt a shiver creep up my spine.

He laughed. "You won't believe this, but I didn't know what to do at first. They call it a 'blow job', so I guess I thought that's just what I was supposed to do: blow. But after a while I knew that sucking would feel better for him, so I started sucking."

"Go on."

"At first I was only putting the tip of his dick into my mouth. I was afraid to let him go in more than that. Have you ever heard of the 'gag reflex'?"

"No. What's that?"

"It's this instinct we all have. Basically, it's to keep you from choking to death. If anything rubs against the back of your throat you automatically start to throw up. It's natural. Some people have a very low tolerance and I'm one of them. That's why I only let him in so far."

"Go on."

"As you keep doing it you get more and more used to it. First, I'd take him in as far as I could, for as long as I could. But when I couldn't stand it anymore, I'd pull away and wait till I was ready for another try. I kept repeating this, and the more I did it, the easier it got to take him in further. Pretty soon, I could take him all the way in."

"All the way? But your mouth isn't big enough!"

"No. That's why you have to relax these muscles here at the back of your throat. You can overcome your gag reflex with practice, and pretty soon it's nothing. You can let him slide all the way in, even down your throat."

"God!"

"You can practice with carrots and stuff. Anyone can learn to do it."

"What makes you think anyone *wants* to do it?"

He shrugged. "I don't know. Maybe you don't believe me. Maybe you think I'm making all this up."

"No way. But if someone could overhear us now, I wonder what they'd think."

"They'd beat the crap out of me, of course."

"Did you let him come in your mouth?"

"Not at first. But after the first few times, I wanted to see what it was like. So I let him."

"Can you tell when he's ready to come?"

"You can usually feel the excitement building up. The balls shrink up tight. Then the dick seems to grow even bigger and hotter just before he shoots off."

"God! And what was it like when it happened?"

"I almost choked on it the first time. I didn't expect there to be so much. I spent the next ten minutes coughing my guts out because it almost went down my lungs. It sounds funny now, but believe me, it wasn't funny when it was happening. I felt sick for a long time afterwards, like I wanted to throw up. It was terrible. But eventually I learned how not to gag on it anymore."

"How does it taste?"

"Kind of salty... like a warm, salty gob in your mouth."

"Ugh!"

"I know. That's how I was at first. But once you get over the taste and the texture, you even start to like it."

I felt faint.

"You seem fascinated, Guy."

"Well... anyone would be. I mean, who doesn't like to hear about forbidden things?"

"You're right," he said. "I think most boys are interested in it, only they're afraid to admit it. Deep down, they want to know what it's like... doing it with another boy."

"You're probably right."

"What about you?"

"Me?"

"Yeah."

I looked at my feet.

"You're turning red, Guy."

"It's because of all the crazy things we're saying."

"I only want to know the truth. Well?"

"Well, what?"

"Don't you want to know what it's like?"

"I don't like that smirk on your face. Since you put it like that, no, I don't."

"Oh. I thought you might."

I was taken aback. "What makes you say that?"

He didn't answer for a long time. And then he started talking in a softer voice. "You know, all through eighth grade I thought you had a crush on me."

"What?"

"Yeah. The way you were teasing me, the way you got your friends to gang up on me. Underneath all that cruelty, I detected something else. I thought of your bullying as a sort of courtship."

I shook my head in denial. He went on: "But once we got to high school, you started having all those girlfriends. I was watching you from the sidelines, so to speak... Wendy, Judy, Vanessa, the new girl I saw you with yesterday. I figured you couldn't be gay. So I kind of gave up, even though a part of me—"

"—was still in love with me?"

He laughed. "It isn't like that. Stop thinking of it as a boy-girl kind of thing. It isn't like that at all. It's something you'd have no idea of."

The thought that he'd once felt attracted to me (and perhaps still did) sent a surge of joy into my heart.

He got up from the floor and walked back to the window to close the curtains. It had gotten so dark inside the room that the sky outside actually seemed brighter than it had been a few minutes ago. He looked over his shoulder at me. "You remember that time in the music room, way back in junior high?"

"Yeah. What about it?"

"You were so much more aggressive about things back then. Now you're scared."

"I was a kid then—curious... just discovering things. I don't know what made me do it. Just fooling around, I guess."

"You wanna know something, Guy? I was actually ready to do it. Till you chickened out."

"I didn't chicken out. I told you I was only fooling around with you."

"Well, a little while ago, you said you were curious about it. Was that 'fooling around', too?"

"I said curious, yeah... but curious in an abstract way. That doesn't mean I want to actually do it with someone."

I found myself trembling but he didn't seem to notice it—he seemed silently intent upon something, perhaps the memory of that moment in the music room. His mouth suddenly twisted into an amused grin.

"Who knows?" he said. "If things had turned out differently at the time, you might have had your curiosity satisfied long ago. More than your curiosity."

"Get outta here...."

Perhaps it was the effect of the marijuana, but I could visualize clearly what it would be like to have him suck me off. I could picture it vividly, down to the tiniest details...

Suddenly, he sighed loudly and said: "All this *talking* about it..."

His statement hung suspended in the air, unfinished.

I glanced nervously at the bedroom door. It was getting dangerous to remain here much longer. I knew exactly what he was leading up to, and my desire to escape the room became overwhelming.

When I looked back at him he was gazing straight at me. His smile was so suggestive that I sensed his desire like a keen smell. I felt dizzy.

The room had acquired a tingly, vibratory clarity; it suddenly became filled with menace.

I got up. "Listen, I have to go now. I—"

"I know, I know. You suddenly remembered something you had to do, right?" His faint smile had turned mocking. It looked pasted on; he was smiling with an effort. My stomach ached.

Somehow I found my way to the door. My fingers clawed for the doorknob in the dark; I found it, turned it. The hallway outside was even darker than the room but I managed to find my way down the stairs and out the back door, to freedom. But even as my feet began running, my feeling of release was tumultuously mixed with the keen ache of regret.

5. The Heterosexual Blues

From my room I heard the telephone ringing. I listened as the vacuum cleaner was shut off and my mother went to answer it. When there was no knock on my door after some time, I relaxed. It wasn't for me.

Mark had called my house several times since that afternoon in his bedroom, but when I refused to come to the phone each time, he finally realized I had no wish to see him again. I had no other choice. He might get the wrong idea about me and I couldn't take that risk.

I wished now that I had never pressed him to confess about his homosexuality. While it had still been an exciting possibility, I could live with it, but now that it was a fact, I could no longer think of him as a friend. He was a danger now, a threatening temptation to give in to my baser instincts. In his bedroom I had come dangerously close to stepping over the line. Too close.

I didn't trust myself to remain indifferent to what he represented. His confession had contaminated me, weakening my defenses, sapping my strong resolve to remain pure. The surest way of building my defenses up again was to avoid seeing him. It was as simple as that.

At the same time, it was thrilling to know that Mark *was* a real faggot, that he had actually done the things I only fantasized about. It gave me the ability to delight in them vicariously, with no danger to myself.

But the games I played, and the things I fantasized about, were done with the consciousness that I was playing with fire. The thrills I experienced came from that very knowledge: I was stepping into forbidden territory and breaking taboos.

His confession also changed forever the dynamics of our relationship. I now had the upper hand: the power to tell someone else about his secret. But somehow I didn't want to tell anyone yet, perhaps ever. Just the possession of his secret was satisfaction enough.

The telephone rang again. I held my breath and waited.

There was a knock on my door.

"Guy. Telephone."

"If it's Mark, tell him I'm out."

"It's Jack."

"All right."

I went out to answer the phone. It had been quite a while since I'd last talked to Jack. In fact, not since the end of the school year.

"Jack?"

"Hi, Guy. Are you free this afternoon?" He sounded a little breathless.

"Sure. What's up?"

"Mind if drop by in a little while?"

"No problem."

I wondered what all the mystery was.

Ten minutes later there was a roaring sound out front, and the sound of a horn. I looked out and saw Jack getting off a motorcycle. I ran outside.

By the time I got there, Jack was standing beside the motorcycle and grinning broadly. "How do you like my new bike?"

"It's a beauty!"

I admired its chrome finish, every little piece of which had been buffed until it shone with a high polish. The glittering silver contrasted with the tasteful flat metallic black of the rest of the body. The teardrop-shaped fuel tank was shot through with the thinnest piping of gold. It was a dream vehicle, a sexy symbol which was the very embodiment of tough masculinity.

I thought of all the lucky boys at school who already owned bikes. During lunch break and at the end of each day—with an appreciative audience of younger boys looking on—they would fondle, stroke, tinker at their machines with an exhibitionistic delight. I had often dreamed of the day when I would have my own motorcycle and be allowed to join that select group of boys in their black leather jackets and boots, who wore their maleness so casually, so carelessly, like a scar earned in a knife fight.

Jack could tell I was impressed. "Wanna go for a ride on it?"

"All right!"

"Where you wanna go?"

"Anywhere. Just get me away from here."

He swung a long leg over the saddle and kicked up the stand. "Go ahead. Climb on back."

He waited as I carefully settled myself in behind him, then turning the key in the ignition, he pushed the bike away from the curb. With a press of the automatic starter button, the engine whined briefly before exploding into life.

I felt my body vibrate in sympathetic rhythm.

"Hang on."

I clutched at his waist as we shot off with a huge lurch and I felt my heart leap up with a thump. The vibrations of the powerful bike were like heavy, throbbing caresses along my thighs and buttocks. The leather of the seat felt warm and tingly between my legs.

We shot straight through the Liddell Street intersection. As we rounded the slow curve leading past the park, I had to lean with the bike, dangerously low and close to the pavement. By now the road was a blur of gray and the scenery was indistinguishable from the giddy excitement in my heart. Memoryless, I lived only with the sensations of the immediate moment. I was intensely aware of my own body—the racing of my heart as it pumped blood through my veins, the muscles of my whole body clenching in an ecstatic spasm.

My hands which had been clamped on either side of Jack's hips gradually eased forward until they met and clasped in front of his stomach. In fact I was a little frightened at the eye-blurring speed with which we barrelled past cars and took turns leaning over so far that I felt I could reach out and touch the pavement.

The masterful way Jack controlled this splendid machine gave him an added status in my eyes. I didn't feel the slightest resistance to clinging tightly to his back. The combination of the bike's vibrations with the hard feel of his body against mine was beginning to excite me. I pressed myself even harder against his body. As we leaned and dipped with every undulation in the road, I felt at one with the machine and with Jack. One entity, we shot through the heart of the universe.

When we finally slowed to a stop, we were at the intersection leading to the on-ramp of the freeway. I tapped his shoulder and shouted above the engine's roar: "Where are we going?"

He didn't seem to hear me. Apparently my words were carried away by the wind. The light turned green and we shot up the ramp and onto the wide, windy freeway.

As we roared down the fast lane, tears streamed back from my eyes, horizontally across my temple. I could feel the adrenalin pumping through my body, making me shiver.

Suddenly it seemed to me I was experiencing something that had happened long ago, somewhere in another time. It might have been something in a movie. And then I remembered.

It was all the way back in elementary school. There was a story in my second-grade textbook which, for some reason, I was never able to forget. It went something like this:

As darkness falls, a black horse comes galloping, galloping from out of the gathering dusk. It approaches a village and halts outside a farmhouse door. A little boy comes crawling out a window, sleepily rubbing his eyes, and climbs onto its back. The horse gallops on.

Next it comes to a town, where it halts outside another house. A little girl this time comes out, almost sleepwalking, clambers up onto the black horse's spacious back.

And the horse gallops on... on and on, from village to village, town to town, city to city. And at each place, children climb up onto its back, where they curl up and fall asleep. They look so safe and secure there.

No matter how many children climb onto its back, there is always room for one more. For every child is welcome.

And the horse gallops on and on through the night, never tiring, never slowing, inexorably onward, forever galloping, galloping towards the end of the night. And the horse's name is Dream.

At this moment, I felt that Jack's bike was but another version of that fabulous horse. I could easily imagine the two of us riding off into the sunset on it, to the next town, and the next, all across America, in the night, all but invisible, going from town to town, city to city, leaving everything behind, picking up boys like me, befriending them, moving on. Jack was my heterosexual prince, come to rescue me from my fears and temptations, from my illicit desires... from Mark.

There had to be boys like me all across America who wanted to be rescued, and they would be waiting for us. We would roar into town to pick them up and carry them away, for there was always room for one more.

With a slight lurch and a change in the engine's pitch, the bike abruptly slowed down. Jack was heading for the next off-ramp. As we wound down along a curving road that led toward the far side of the Wilds, I recognized the old airport road, little used now since the new freeway bypass had been built.

We cruised for a while down this road until suddenly Jack turned off and steered down a dirt path which gradually got more and more overgrown with weeds. When we could go no farther without damaging the bike we stopped.

All around us was scrub grass. The sun was setting, staining everything a washed-out dust color. Gradually I began to recognize where we were.

This was the desolate stretch of scrubland west of the city where we'd often gone exploring as little boys, so long ago. The boulders embedded here and there like monumental markers in the parched scrubland made the place look desolate. Except for the railroad tracks which sliced a shiny welt through the landscape, there was absolutely no sign of life.

We got off the bike and Jack parked and locked it. There was a slight wind. Jack continued up the path on foot, and I followed. The tall weeds through which we made our way bent and swayed in the breeze. My light windbreaker whipped out behind me and climbed up my back.

"Why'd we come out here, Jack?"

He didn't answer. His earlier euphoria about showing off his new bike had seemed to evaporate sometime during the ride. He was in a somber mood now. I stopped asking him questions and silently followed.

After about ten minutes, we were stopped by a barbed-wire fence which had never been there before. A sign nearby informed us that it had been erected by the city to fence off a proposed land development project. We went along its side until we came to a spot where trampled weeds left a smooth clearing. Searching the ground nearby I found a stick to prop apart two strands of barbed wire so we could climb through.

We slid down into the dried gully bed and climbed up the opposite bank. Slipping on treacherous loose stones and gravel, we made our way up the shallow trail leading to the old swimming hole. Soon the familiar boulders loomed just ahead. As we skirted the lip of the reservoir and made toward the shadow of the huge rocks, I recognized the old nooks and caves we used to play in.

Just ahead was the flat ledge from which we used to dive. When I spotted it I felt a sharp pang of nostalgia. Somehow it looked smaller, less forbidding than it used to, but perhaps it was because it was getting dark. I thought of that long, heart-gripping plunge and the jarring slap of water which always hit my butt.

I peered over the edge.

The water—so cool and refreshing in memory—was gone. Nothing was down below but scraggly weeds clumped together, their shadows lengthened by the setting sun.

"It's gone," I said. "What happened to the water?"

I lowered myself until I was sitting on the edge.

"Remember? The city dammed up some streams to re-route them to Echo Lake in the park."

"Oh yeah, that's right. I didn't think it would affect this place, though."

Far off toward the freeway, the cars glinted, flashing their windshields in the sun like message signals as they whipped along with a dull roaring sound. In the other direction rolled miles and miles of empty wasteland.

"Changed, isn't it?" said Jack.

"Yeah. We used to have so much fun out here."

"Didn't we, though?" He looked a little depressed.

I wondered what was behind his strange mood. "Did you suddenly felt nostalgic for it? I get like that sometimes myself."

He didn't answer. After a long silence, he said, "You still going with Vanessa, Guy?"

"No. We broke up." I laughed. "Now you can have a shot at her. With this bike of yours, it's a cinch. She's bound to fall for you."

"Yeah." He sounded tired.

"What's the matter, Jack? You're acting so weird lately."

"I got a girl pregnant."

"What?" I stared at him as the usual banal questions whirled through my mind: who? when? where? But I didn't know what to say.

He didn't even wait for me to ask. "It was Marybeth. Do you know her?"

"Yeah. Of course."

"I didn't use a rubber."

I thought of him dancing with Marybeth on the night of the Green and White Dance. He'd looked so happy and confident then— it seemed a lifetime away, locked away in a past so distant it was like fiction. Now he seemed so adultly tired. What had happened to him had happened to other boys as well—it was the gamble they all took. All of them, that is, except me. My own worries seemed so trivial now next to Jack's. As always, he was far ahead of me. I was still the little kid with the little kid's preoccupations, and he was the adult. I would forever be unable to catch up with him.

"What are you gonna do?" I asked.

"Get an abortion. That's the only thing we can do."

"Where? How?"

"At an abortion clinic. Or somewhere. There are places where it can be done. Her parents don't even have to know about it."

"That seems so drastic..."

"Yeah. I thought about it long and hard. I actually thought of having the baby. But there's no way. For either of us. I want to go to college, and so does she. In the end... well, we decided to go through with the abortion."

"Is it very expensive?"

"I don't know. Whatever it costs can be covered by selling my bike."

"But you just bought it!"

"I know. At least I got to ride it for a week..."

"When did you find out about the pregnancy?"

"Just two days ago. You're the first person I've told. In fact, I wasn't even sure if I was gonna tell you or not today. But I had to tell someone. It's been hell living with it."

"I can imagine."

He was silent for a long time. When he spoke again, his voice was a dull monotone, as if he were talking to himself, as if I weren't even there.

"You know, it's not an easy choice to make. It's harder for the girl, of course, but it's also hard for the boy. And we used to joke about it, too, before... It's terrible just to think of it. Do you know, they actually scrape away a part of the uterus? It's permanently damaged afterwards. She'll never be the same. And the baby. It's a living thing they kill. A human being."

He was looking down at the ground and I felt helpless.

"Damn," he muttered as if to himself. "One little shot of pleasure and you have to pay for it the rest of your life."

"Take it easy, Jack. It can't be that bad. It happens all the time. You hear about it all the time."

"Yeah, to other people. This is me. I'm talking about *me*."

"Sorry."

He looked hard at me "Listen, Guy. Promise me one thing. Promise me you'll always use a rubber when you fuck a girl. Okay? Don't do like I did. It isn't worth the extra pleasure."

"Sure, Jack. I promise."

"That's all I wanted to say, I guess. That, and showing you my bike."

I thought how little likely it was that I would ever have to fulfill the promise, for I was protected by something so much more powerful than a mere rubber sheath. He would laugh himself silly if he ever learned.

"It's getting dark. Should we head back?"

"All right."

Without another word we walked back to the bike and returned to town.

* * *

As he was about to drop me off in front of my house, I noticed two boys walking down the sidewalk. Jack, too, was peering in their direction.

"Who are they?" I asked.

"One of them looks like Mark Warren."

"Who's the guy with him?"

"Guy named Alex Benniker."

"Never heard of him."

"Plays basketball for St. Mary's. Good player, too. I didn't know he was one of 'them', though. Just goes to show—you never can tell."

"Yeah." We'd pulled up in my driveway, and I got off.

Mark and his friend seemed to be looking our way.

"Look at those faggots," said Jack musingly. "In a way, they're lucky, I guess. They can fuck each other all they want and not worry about anything."

"Yeah."

"I almost wish I was a faggot myself."

"No you don't, Jack. Don't say that."

"I know. Well, see you later, Guy."

"Yeah."

He pulled out of the driveway with a wave and shot down the street, roaring.

By now Mark and his friend were getting close. Alex was a tall boy with curly brown hair and he was bouncing a basketball lazily as he walked along, occasionally twirling around, feinting past imaginary opponents and shooting at phantom baskets. Beside him Mark was dangling a gym bag and laughing at his antics.

My first thought was to duck into the garage to avoid having to meet them. But after Jack's confession, everything to do with

Mark seemed so silly; my fear of his tempting me seemed so immature, so childish. Some of Jack's sad maturity had rubbed off onto me, making me feel superior, above it all. I wasn't afraid of Mark anymore.

As they approached me, Mark's face froze and he stared straight ahead, looking right past me as if I weren't there. Alex noticed this change in him and became cautious. This gave me confidence.

"Hi, Mark," I said in an exaggeratedly friendly manner. I looked at Alex, then back at Mark in what I hoped was an insinuating manner.

Mark didn't answer. As they walked past me, I noticed the glance they exchanged, and the subsequent look of suspicion Alex cast toward me. They continued on without a word, as if nothing had happened.

I looked after them, smiling, but felt a sudden surge of anger boil up inside me. My limbs ached with the desire for violence.

I wondered when they'd become friends. Mark had never mentioned Alex to me before. But of course it had nothing to do with me anymore. Mark was free to find a new friend with whom he could play his games. A new friend he could tempt in his bedroom.

The lousy faggots.

I felt the blood drain from my face.

I went into my house and locked myself in my bedroom. After I felt enough time had passed, I came out to the living room. I still knew Mark's telephone number from way back in junior high school.

Mark answered the phone after a couple of rings. "Hello? Warren residence."

"Mark? This is Guy."

"Oh. How have you *been*?"

I winced at the fake syrupy tone of his voice; the irony in it sounded so contrived that I felt embarrassed for him. "I've been just fine, Mark. As if you didn't snub me today."

"Who's the one who refused to answer my calls for the past two weeks?"

"I was busy."

"Apparently so."

"Since when were you friends with Alex Benniker?"

"Alex? What's it to *you*?" He suddenly sounded defensive.

"Just curious. It's just that I didn't realize Alex was 'like that'."

"You don't even *know* Alex, and here you are making accusations about him. I'm surprised at you. I thought you were the one who was so open-minded about people's sexual preferences. Alex and I are just good friends"

"Well, even if he's not queer, I'm surprised he isn't afraid of being seen with you."

"That's none of your business."

"Listen. I'm only telling you this for your own good. You shouldn't be making yourself so obvious. A lot of guys in school would beat you up just for that. You're taking a big risk."

"I'm not worried. They're just jealous, that's all. Most bullies are just that—jealous. Like a certain bully I knew back in the eighth grade."

"You'd better stop your insinuations—if you don't want me to beat you up myself."

"I thought you were over all that. Some friend you turned out to be."

"Friend? You mean you still consider us friends?"

"Sure. I mean we can still see each other, even though you know about me. In fact, now that you know me for what I am, our relationship will be more honest."

"Listen, Mark—you won't..."

"What?"

"You won't tell anyone about what we talked about in your bedroom, will you? I mean, I trust you on this. You have to give me your word. If anyone found out about it..."

"Am I hearing you right?"

"Listen, I personally don't care if you're gay. But other people might suspect something if I keep seeing you after knowing you are. That's what I'm worried about. People might get the wrong impression."

A near-hysterical laughter rang in the earpiece. It went on for a long time before he managed to control himself.

"So that's it. Is that why you were so afraid of meeting me since then? I could have saved you all your worry if you'd only met me. Listen, Guy, I'm sorry about what happened in my room. I guess that's what got you all upset. Don't worry about it; I just got a little bit carried away—I must have misunderstood your signals."

"Signals? I wasn't giving out any signals. I don't know what you're talking about."

He laughed again, this time much more gently. "Guy, you don't know how silly you sound. But I can't talk right now, my parents are home. Listen, anytime you wanna talk, just drop by. Both my parents work, so I have the house to myself on weekdays till seven. Come by whenever you want to. All right?"

I didn't say anything.

"Bye, Guy."

He hung up.

For some reason, the only thing I felt was relief; I felt exactly like a boy who's been begging and begging a girl for a date, and she's finally relented.

6. Boys Who Never Kiss and Tell

I was in the Sunnyside Mall looking for new clothes when I spotted Mark walking down the plaza. As I ducked behind a pillar to hide from him, I noticed he was with someone—Alex Benniker, again. They were talking together and laughing. Apparently they'd just finished watching a movie, for they were among a large crowd of people pouring out of the theater's opened doors.

I watched them walk past the display window, then slipped outside and began following them. With all the shoppers in the mall it was easy to keep the two boys in sight without being seen myself. But when I tried to get close enough to catch what they were saying, it became too risky.

They seemed to be heading to the East parking lot. I'd parked my own car in the South parking lot, so it would be a little tricky to tail them once they'd gotten in their car.

As they left the mall by the East exit, I posted myself by the door and noted their direction. Scanning the rows of cars, I spotted Mark's red MG. They were obviously heading toward it.

I made a dash toward the South exit and rushed out to my own car, got in, slammed the door and started it up. By the time I got to the East parking lot, Mark's MG was just pulling out into traffic on Kennedy Drive. As I maneuvered my way toward the intersection, an old Volkswagen van suddenly backed out of a parking space in front of me, blocking my way.

I had to content myself with noting the direction Mark's car took. I would never be able to tail it.

When I finally got to Kennedy Drive, I took the direction they'd gone, wondering where they might be going. For some reason, it had become very important to me to verify that the two boys were having a sexual relationship. But unless I virtually caught them in the act, Mark would be able to deny everything. I dreamed of catching them coming out of a motel room or something...

I'd been driving along for some time, keeping a sharp lookout for the tell-tale red color of the MG, before I remembered Mark telling me that both his parents were usually out during the weekdays. I cursed my own carelessness. If my guess was correct, Mark and Alex would be heading there right now.

I made a turn at the next light and doubled back toward Mark's house. It seemed to take forever to get there. The first thing I saw as I pulled over to the curb was Mark's red MG parked out in front of his house. I felt my throat go dry as I imagined the two boys inside the house, perhaps inside Mark's bedroom.

I shut off the engine and began my wait.

But with the air conditioner off, it began to get uncomfortably hot. I rolled down the windows to let in a little breeze. From where I was parked, I could see Mark's upstairs window. The curtains were open. That meant they probably weren't in the bedroom. Or if they were, they weren't worried about being seen.

I got out of the car and approached the house. It appeared to be all quiet. I suddenly pictured them in a very compromising position, and myself ringing the doorbell to strike fear into them.

I went to the front door and, peering around to make sure no one could see me, rang the bell. Even as I was standing before his door, I still wasn't quite sure why I'd come.

The door opened and Mark was standing there. He didn't seem at all surprised to see me. I had expected quite a different reaction—panic or confusion, perhaps.

"Guy. I didn't expect you to drop in."

"I guess not. Especially since you're so busy now."

"Busy? What do you mean?"

"You know what I mean."

"No I don't. What's the matter, Guy? You look agitated."

"I saw you with Alex."

"Oh?" He seemed amused. "Yes. I dropped him off at home just now. Why didn't you say something to me?"

"Just friends, huh? I thought you said you and Alex were just friends. What were you doing going to the movies together?"

"Can't two friends go to the movies together anymore without being accused of homosexuality?"

"He's inside right now, isn't he?"

"No way. No one's here now but me, Guy."

"Bullshit."

"If you don't believe me, you can come in and check. You don't know how silly you sound."

He stepped back to let me in. I stepped inside the hallway and looked around.

"Go ahead," he said. "The living room's that way, Sherlock Holmes..."

I peered around at all the downstairs rooms.

"He's up in your bedroom," I said.

"Go on up and check."

"I'm not going up there."

"Listen, the best way to find out is to call him at home, because that's where he is right now." He picked up the telephone on the sideboard. "I'll tell you his number."

"Never mind."

In a taunting voice he said: "You know something, Guy? You sound like you're jealous or something."

"Jealous? Why should I be jealous? I ain't the fag."

"Well, you're acting for all the world like a jealous lover. I didn't know your feelings for me were that strong."

"Get lost. Stop trying to deceive me with your stupid fag jokes."

"But you forget—I *am* a fag. I can say those things now. At least, in front of you."

I glared at him but he only tisked his tongue.

"Listen. It doesn't make much sense standing here and talking like this. Why don't you sit down and make yourself more comfortable? I was just fixing myself a sandwich. Would you like one?"

My heart began to race but my voice, amazingly, remained quite calm. "You're not gonna—try anything, are you?"

"Try anything? Like what?"

"Like make a pass at me like you did last time. It's not gonna ever happen again, right? Because if it does, I'm gonna beat the crap out of you."

He laughed. "Don't worry. Nothing's gonna happen that you don't want to happen. After all, you're stronger than me, aren't you? How can I make you do anything against your will?"

"I guess you're right."

He looked at me questioningly. "Look, I don't want to be enemies. I want to stay friends. Even though you seem to be so upset about my sexual leanings. How can I help that? I like boys. That's all there is to it."

I didn't move.

"Why do you feel the need to bully me just because I like to suck dick?"

I felt a film come over my eyes. At his words, an erection began blossoming in my pants, so sudden and unasked for that it was painful. And something told me he knew of my predicament—

that he'd purposely caused it with his provocative choice of words.

I swallowed.

Tiny shivers were passing through my body. The more I tried to calm myself, the harder my dick strained. I wondered if he noticed. When I looked at him there was an amused smile on his face. At once my defenses came up.

"What's so funny?"

"The way you have your... you shouldn't try to hide it like that."

"I'm not trying to hide anything."

"Yes you are. You have your hand cupped over it."

"No I don't."

I moved aside my hand and looked down, and to my embarrassment, saw my excitement clearly outlined under my jeans.

Far from showing contempt, however, Mark was gazing thoughtfully, almost sadly at it. This calm scrutiny only made things worse. Despite all my mental entreaties I felt myself harden even more. "I can't help it," I said weakly.

I sat down abruptly to try to hide my embarrassment.

"Don't you find it difficult sometimes to keep from getting a hard-on, especially when you feel uncomfortable? Like in the locker room, changing for PE class? I mean, just the act of undressing is a turn-on, isn't it?"

I thought of the rumors I'd heard about his getting hard in the showers back in junior high school.

"I can manage," I said gruffly.

"Not everyone can." He laughed. "But I don't take PE anymore so I don't have to worry."

He looked at me for a while without saying anything. Then, out of the blue, he asked softly, "Tell me the real reason why you came here today."

"I *told* you."

"That isn't it and you know it. I think I know the real reason, but you're too scared to say it—maybe even too scared to think it."

"And what is that, may I ask?"

"You want to take me up on my offer. Isn't that it?"

"Don't make me laugh."

"You just don't want to admit it to yourself."

"Boy, are you ever wrong. You don't know how wrong you are, Warren."

"Oh?"

He stood by the coffee table regarding me with an enigmatic look, his weight concentrated provocatively on one leg.

"That afternoon in my room. You wouldn't have minded, would you? If I'd gone ahead and done it."

I didn't trust my voice enough to speak.

"Well?" he prodded.

A strange feeling began to overwhelm me. It suddenly seemed as though everything was taking place in a dream. I felt remote, detached from it all, caught in the middle of a hallucination.

"I can't figure you out, Guy." His voice seemed to come from far away.

I could barely see his face. He came over and sat down on the sofa near me; I jumped up and moved to another chair. I wanted to run from the room but felt too weak to make the effort. I couldn't budge from the room.

"Close the curtains," I said. "I don't wanna be seen here."

"No one can see us here from the street. Besides, there's a tree blocking the window."

Feeling my mouth go dry, I whispered: "Close them."

Tisking his tongue, he whisked the curtains shut, plunging the room into darkness. He walked over to the side-table lamp and switched it on. Its green shade bathed the room in a summery haze.

I took a deep breath. My heart was still hammering wildly, and little tremors were chasing themselves all up and down my body. I didn't want him to see how nervous I was.

"What time do your—your parents come home?" I asked. My throat was all dry.

"We have the whole house to ourselves until seven tonight."

I stared at the curtained window.

He sighed. "It's so hot in here with the curtains closed."

"Why don't you turn on the air-conditioner?"

Ignoring me, he stretched both arms over his head and began peeling off his t-shirt. I watched it slip up and away, revealing smooth skin whose whiteness was blemished only by two button-like nipples, pale pink in color. Flipping the t-shirt away, he turned to face me. "That feels so much better."

"Put your shirt back on, damn it."

"Guy, you look so cute when you're angry."

"I said put your shirt on."

"I don't have to. It's my house." He sat down on the sofa.

"Do you want to know the truth about me and Alex?"

"Yes."

"Alex isn't gay. But he's very open-minded about certain things."

"Meaning?"

"He lets me suck his dick."

I felt my face flush. "Are you two lovers? Are you going steady or something?"

"No, silly. Like I keep telling you, it's not like those boy-girl things. It doesn't work that way with us. Besides, there's a certain other boy I like more. I only wish he were more sympathetic."

I didn't say a word.

"Can you guess who he is?"

I swallowed.

"Will you at least let me sit down next to you? I'm not gonna bite you or anything."

"No."

He came over anyway and knelt on the floor near me, resting an arm on the chair but making no move. "Well, Guy?"

"Well what?"

"Won't you let me do it to you?"

"................"

"Is it yes or no?"

I couldn't say a word, so he pressed on: "I'll do everything. You just sit there and let me do all the work."

I shook my head.

"Well then just tell me this: is it completely out of the question? If not today, then some day in the future."

I took another deep breath, feeling as if I were getting ready to plunge into ice-cold water. "It's not com*plete*ly out of the question."

"Well, if it's not completely out of the question, that means it's yes. Or is my logic getting confused by my desires?"

Before I could stop him his hand was moving toward my belt buckle. The speed with which he was getting down to business was dizzying. I stopped his hand. If he undid my pants, there would be no hiding my own desire.

"I can do it myself."

Self-consciously I toyed with the fly. My fingers felt clumsy and unresponsive. I told myself it would be no different from undressing for PE class and tried to believe it. I remembered how shy

I'd been the first time I had to get naked in front of other boys.

Seeing my hesitation, he sighed impatiently. "Here, let me do it."

I let him undo my jeans and offered no resistance. He seemed unbelievably calm about the whole thing. Without the slightest trace of self-consciousness, and with a certain practiced skill, he pulled my briefs down and let my erection spring free.

Now that I was naked below the waist, and so brazenly exposed, I felt a strange sense of ease, relaxation.

A dim light glinted off the tiny clear bead of liquid shivering on the tip of the glans like a pure tear.

"God, this is embarrassing."

I started to cover myself with my hand, but Mark gently dissuaded me by blocking it with his own hand: "I wanna see it."

He gazed calmly at my erection for a long time. It felt good to be able to let him. And then he touched me.

I gave myself up to the shy touch of his fingers, feeling a curious release from inhibition. The sensation of another boy's hands exploring me with such brazen intimacy made me feel as if I'd relinquished ownership of my own penis. I felt pleasantly lazy, almost drowsy. I thought of the time I'd done it with Bobby, but somehow this was so different. Mark's slightly damp fingers became more and more sure of themselves; the gentle exploration had become a subtle but rhythmic kneading.

His head was bent down to watch his own fingers manipulating the loose skin softly back and forth. I closed my eyes to better enjoy his fingers' gentle stroking. And then I felt something different.

It was almost imperceptible at first, so unnoticeable that I had to open my eyes to make sure. His prodding finger which had been delicately spreading the tip-liquid around and around had at some point—exactly when, I would never know—been replaced by his tongue. With him bent over my lap like that, all I could see was the top of his head with its dark hair spiralling out from the crown in a swirl pattern. But there was no mistaking the soft kissing play of his lips along the rim of my glans.

I felt an unbelievable drunken clarity; not wanting to miss a thing, I leaned my head down so that I could relish the sight. As in a dream I saw his half-open mouth in close juxtaposition to my glans. His eyelids looked slack and reptilian. As his lips pouted into a kiss again and descended, I felt a tightness cup the tip of my dick, then widen, flowing around to completely cover the head until I was engulfed in warmth. I closed my eyes as the muscles in my dick contracted in a surge.

A compact tightness, warm and wet, moved slowly down my shaft... down, down, all the way down, until I was engulfed. Then his head moved back up, and coolness returned. For a moment, his head remained balanced at the peak, and then the warmth descended again until I was almost all the way in and I could feel the inside of his cheek. Then it got cool again, and then warm, cool and warm. His head was moving up and down in a gentle bobbing motion. Cool and warm alternated in even strokes. He began rocking his body back and forth with the motion, his cheeks puckering as he sucked. As I watched the visible part of my penis alternately lengthening and shortening, it felt as if it were being dipped rhythmically into a warm bath.

I'm doing it, I thought. I'm finally doing it. I'm getting a blow job. This was what was written on the boys' room walls, the dirty little secret that was whispered about boys like Mark. Yet I felt a curious lack of excitement at the thought, only a tense worry. I couldn't shake the feeling that someone was spying on us, and even peered around to make sure we weren't being watched. The doors were unlocked, I knew. But I also knew I could pull my pants back up at the slightest sign of danger—they were bunched up down around my ankles.

Mark had stopped sucking. His pink tongue now flattened against the underside of my shaft. I felt it slide up my length, its slow tacky progress so discernible along my throbbing vein there. Then, holding my shaft lightly with one hand he ran his tongue down again along its underside until he was snuffling down near the base. I felt the tip of his nose on my balls, and couldn't suppress a groan as the velvet lap of his tongue crept right up between them. His wet kisses were making my balls tumble and draw up in reaction. Then his soft mobile lips traced a snail's trail from root to tip like a hungry little fish's mouth nibbling shyly at proffered bait but not biting. The warm tickle of his tongue played over my glans, nuzzling the underside where it felt best. A tingle shot down from the back of my head all the way to my feet, making me curl and clench my toes. I groaned aloud.

I pulled my shirt off and tossed it aside—any cloth against my skin seemed to deaden the intensity of my pleasure. Mark had returned to his steady, even, almost machine-like bobbing, with his fingers encircling the base of my dick firmly for support.

I had never been bathed in such pleasure before, yet I didn't dare lose my self-control. A part of me wanted to let go but the other part kept a tight control over my reactions. I wished I could say stop, yet I wanted more, wanted to go to the limit, to the utmost limit.

I can't come, I told myself, I can't come. I mustn't.

And yet I was quickly losing all control. My fear and tenseness were melting away under the mounting laps of pleasure. I groaned again. My fingers went to Mark's hair, ran through its softness in stroking motions. I no longer peered nervously about for possible eye-witnesses but gave myself up, in total submission to my pleasure.

I knew it was a pleasure that had been experienced by countless other boys before me... Alex... Ron... Dave... and boys whose names I didn't even know, going all the way back to junior high school, long before the music room episode when I'd almost joined their number, so long ago now. It didn't seem possible that he'd been so afraid to utter that incriminating phrase.

And then I looked down and saw Mark's face like a heavy-lidded stranger's looking bloated and slack with lust, and felt a sudden revulsion, a recoiling as from a creature out of a swamp. He immediately sensed the change in me and stopped what he was doing. He looked up at me.

"What's the matter, Guy?"

"Nothing."

"Are you disgusted with me? You're thinking what a faggot I am, right?"

"It's not that—" But it was that, undeniably. Instinctively, I glanced at the door. "Did you remember to lock it? Someone could walk right in."

"You're right. If it'll make you any more comfortable, we can go up to my room. Come on."

He picked up his discareded t-shirt and went to the foot of the stairs. He hesitated for a moment and glanced over at me. Then he began to ascend. I watched him disappear up the stairwell. This was my chance to leave if I wanted to. I was free to go. But there was really no decision to make. I did up my jeans again and picked up my t-shirt to join him.

Up in his bedroom, he was standing at the window, having just shut the curtains.

"The lock," he said.

I locked the bedroom door and sat down on the bed.

He looked over at me. "Well?"

"I guess I'm nervous about all this. It's not like it happens every day, you know."

"I wish it did."

"Listen, Mark. You have to promise me not to tell anyone about this."

"Are you crazy? Why would I tell? Who do you think has more to lose, you or me, if I tell?"

"It—it's just that I can't believe what we're doing."

"It happens all the time, Guy. Believe me. You wouldn't believe the number of straight boys who do it. People just don't wanna talk about it, that's all."

"Really?"

"Of course. Heck, there's guys you'd never suspect, who asked me to suck them off. And not only that, but—"

"But?"

He looked straight at me. "Fucked me, too."

The casual way he said it almost made the bottom drop out of my stomach. Just a few weeks ago I wouldn't have believed such things were possible. I would have put them down to the impossible fantasies of some horny boy.

To my incredible shame, I felt my dick stiffen again. Mark saw the effect his words had had on me. I watched the curious look in his eyes as he watched the mound at my crotch grow.

"How about you, Guy? You wanna fuck me, too?"

"Oh God." The answer was so obvious that it seemed ridiculous to try to deny it. Yes. I wanted to fuck him. I wanted it more than anything else in the world. I wanted to fuck this boy who was teasing me so.

Still, I hesitated. For this was something far beyond what we'd just been doing. I sensed a boundary line, beyond which I daren't venture—within whose bounds I was still safely on this side of homosexuality. Technically, I was still a virgin, and as such, neither hetero- nor homosexual. And there was an irrevocable finality about the idea of losing this limbo-like status. I would never afterwards be able to change or erase the moment I stepped across the threshold. If the first time was with a boy, would that brand me forever as a faggot?

And yet didn't they say homosexuality wasn't defined by

just one act?

In adolescence... there is much curiosity... it is normal for friends of the same sex to indulge in mutual explorations...

Even Ron Holmes, with all his girls, had probably tried it at least once. The number of straight boys... guys you'd never suspect...

Even to consummation...

Mark saw my hesitation. "What's the matter?" he said softly. There was a faint smile on his face. Outside the window the trees soughed from a sudden, wayward gust of wind and the curtains billowed slightly.

"Well?"

He made to take off his pants, and then, either from shyness or calculated coquetry, turned away from me to step out of them. I couldn't take my eyes away. This would be the first time I ever saw him naked.

When he turned around he made no effort to hide his own state of arousal. His erection was a little smaller than mine, but almost exactly like it in every other respect.

I felt a sense of relief at seeing him in this condition. He remained standing there, a naughty statue with a beautiful erection. As he noticed me looking at his dick, he twitched it in response, then, smiling devilishly, began pumping himself. I had to giggle.

"Well?" he said. "What are we waiting for?" He came over to the bed with a confident swagger which made me shrivel up inside. "Move over," he ordered softly.

I made room for him.

He plopped down on the bed, face downward, and at the sight of his bared buttocks, I felt the blood rush to my cheeks.

He said something which was lost in a muffled mumble.

"What?"

"I said: 'in the drawer'."

"What is?"

Without turning around, he pointed back to the night table.

I opened the drawer and saw a yellow, half-rolled up tube of KY like the cochlea of a snail. For a moment I was stunned. The KY seemed to stare up at me, the symbol of an irrevocable decision. Mark turned lazily onto his side and held out his hand for it.

I handed it to him and watched as he squeezed out a dab of the translucent jelly. Then he half-turned his body, spread his thighs and reached down between his legs to lubricate himself. The practiced manner with which his finger spread it around in tiny circles, the way it dipped saucily in and out made my stomach flutter.

He handed the tube back to me then snuggled down into the mattress, rumpling the coverlet as he spread his thighs. With his legs fanned out, his butt floated white, while down below, half hidden in shadow, I could see his balls nestled against the mattress.

At this provocative invitation I lost any remaining sense of prudery. Impatiently, I kicked my sneakers off, tossed my socks aside and yanked down my jeans. My briefs were tented out so comically that I was glad Mark couldn't see my excitement. I slipped them down, and with trembling fingers, applied the KY to myself, carefully rubbing on the cool ointment onto my glans until it glistened like a glazed doughnut.

Cocking my knee onto the bed, I knelt between his spread thighs and gazed down, contemplating the smooth curve of his back with its shallow groove down the center. Placing a hand on each buttock, I gently spread the cheeks apart so I could peer at every boy's most secret spot. Glazed and shiny from its coat of jelly, the tiny puckered mouth looked so innocent and helpless.

Taking my dick in hand I guided it down between the plump buttocks until it rested against the anus. The mere touch of skin on skin was almost enough to send me off. I pinched myself tightly just below the glans to temporarily kill my excitement. Even so, a bit of tip-liquid leaked out, like a drop of lemon juice.

Close call.

Without wasting any more time I leaned over his back to position myself, and in response he spread his thighs slightly more to accommodate me.

Everything was going like dream clockwork. I prayed silently that I could contain myself long enough to fully enjoy the fuck. I guided myself down again, this time for good. I knew exactly where.

I worked myself in between the cheeks, the tip of my dick meeting his hole in a shy kiss. I felt the gluey contact and a resistance... and then the soft give as I gently maneuvered in with the slight corkscrew motions I'd learned from my own anal explorations.

Supporting the weight of my body on both hands now, I leaned slowly in, feeling the continuing give as a smooth creeping pinch. From above I gazed down at the magical, dreamed-of sight of my slowly disappearing length being swallowed in as if ingested by a hungry mouth. In—in!—it went, making a slight crackling sound.

When I was halfway in I could go no farther. I paused to catch my breath. Mark had groaned at first but now lay breathing quietly while I gloried in my buried status. With one part of my mind I knew that despite his grunts of pain he had had a lot of practice in order to relax his muscles like this. And I also knew I wasn't the first one. Not by a long shot. The thought of all the other boys who had done this to him got me even more excited. I withdrew myself just a little bit for another try, and as I pulled away saw tiny streaks of brown on my glistening pink.

I leaned in again, a little harder and firmer this time, and closed my eyes to savor the feel of the soft, delicious sink, concentrating on the tight ring-like pinch descending my shaft. His butthole, like a tiny mouth, gripped me the entire way in, in, all the way in, and I thought how perfectly nature had fitted that part of a boy for this wonderful game.

Mark lay quietly beneath me, his head turned to one side, exposing his cheek. For a fleeting moment I wondered how it would feel to put my lips there. My nose was inches away from the back of his head and I could smell his shampoo like an enticing perfume. My breaths ruffled his hair, tickling and pinking his ear. I wished I could stay like this forever.

But the feeling of being inside a boy, all this wealth of bare skin on skin, its sweaty rub, its delicious perversion—was just too much for me.

Leaning low over his back I placed my hands on either side of his shoulders and gave myself up to a steady humping—just as I'd humped my pillow. Listening to the slapping sound of skin on skin, I felt a delicious sensation run from the base of my balls to my own butthole.

To my surprise I soon began to feel a responsive heaving beneath me. The undulations of his hips were producing an unmistakable counter-thrust to meet mine. Again, I thought of all the other boys he'd fucked. He knew how to get the most pleasure out of it.

From my own anal masturbations, I could easily imagine what he was feeling now. I stopped thrusting for a moment and turned both our bodies aside a little so I could see his penis.

It was erect and straining.

A drunken lightheadedness came over me at the sight, a

volitionless freedom, as though I were being carried upon the crest of a wave.

Keeping our bodies half-turned like that so I could continue gazing at his dick, I picked up my speed, shifting into a faster trot, goaded and stung into fury by the saucy upwards bumps of his butt, by his greedy desire to be filled and filled and filled again. In and in, harder and harder—I wanted to go all the way in, up to where the shit came from, shoved in so deep I couldn't go any farther.

The steady creaking of the bed springs seemed distant and unrelated to what we were doing.

I knew the coming orgasm would be the climax of my life... nothing in the world would ever feel as good.

Mark began giving out little feminine grunts as I felt his butthole tighten even more around my dick. Gasping, I threw my head back and bit my lower lip hard as I pumped my pelvis in, deeply, again, again, again, and weak-kneed, felt myself begin to give.

I was coming...

"Oh!"

I came, ejaculating deep into his body, my insides wracked by successive waves of pleasure which reached outward to the farthest corners of my being.

Drained, and almost sobbing, I sank exhausted onto his back, wishing I could sink down forever and ever and disappear. My heart was pounding, and my open mouth gasping for air.

I was still hard inside him, and could feel his sphincter pinching me spasmodically. I remembered the times I'd masturbated myself anally with a banana, a wine bottle, a brush handle, and knew exactly what he was feeling. And I knew how to make it good for him.

Slowly, as slowly as I could, I inched myself out of him, making the good feeling last for him. I could almost feel his pleasure at the withdrawal, the best part after what he'd just been through. I felt his sphincter pinch me in acknowledgement.

And then I was almost all the way out... Mark made a funny strangling noise in his throat just as my dick was squeezed out with a peristaltic push. I heard him gasp and leaned over to watch tiny white droplets spraying out from his dick all over the mattress. I thought it would never end.

Finally he sank down onto the sheet, on top of his come.

I too, sank down again, rolling off and away from his back, feeling the sticky sheet at my back. We both lay breathing heavily like runners after a race. The sound of our breathing seemed to fill the entire world.

I thought of Jack telling me long ago in the hallway, in junior high: "They like to take it up the ass." It seemed so long ago. And now I had done it. Actually done it.

And then it hit me: I wasn't a virgin anymore. I'd just fucked Mark Warren in the ass, and I was a man now. Somehow it didn't seem real. I didn't feel any different.

Next to me Mark stirred, and when I turned my head, found I was gazing straight into his eyes.

He let out a long sigh, then gave a low throaty giggle. "Why didn't you tell me?" he said.

"Tell you what?" A chill crept down my spine.

"You knew exactly what you were doing, didn't you? You knew how to make it good for me. You can't tell me that's the first time you did it. Why didn't you tell me?"

"But that *was* the first time I did it. I swear it!"

"Oh, Guy..."

I hated the insinuating, almost derisive tone of his voice, and knew now that I shouldn't have given in to a moment of weakness, shouldn't have allowed my momentary lapse, shouldn't, in fact, have come to his house at all. But it was too late to regret it now. Much too late.

"It's not what you think," I managed to say.

"Oh? Then welcome to the club."

"What club?"

"Those of us who are unsure of our sexual orientation," he said, as if reciting from a text. He lay on his side curled up, his head pillowed on his hand in regal languor, and he regarded me with a curious and thoughtful expression.

A buzzing sound came to my ears.

I shot up to my feet. "What are you trying to imply?" I felt nothing but a cold, hatchet-like hatred for him now.

"Nothing."

"Yes you are, too! You're calling me a faggot."

We regarded each other with hard, blank faces. Then I reached for my briefs and thrust my legs through the leg-holes, pulled them on.

He suddenly sat up and became placating. "Where are you

going, Guy? Please don't leave just yet. Why do they all want to leave as soon as it's over? Don't make me feel like shit."

"Listen. I only did it 'cause you asked me to. I'm not like you."

He caught at his breath as if he'd been stabbed. "You wanna know something, Willard? You're all the same. All of you. You want it so bad, and when you get it, you just throw me away. Then you slander my name around. It makes you feel so tough, doesn't it?"

"Fuck you, Mark."

"You just did, remember?" He grimaced and turned his face away in angry shame as I pulled on my jeans. And then he whispered again: "You just did."

I didn't know what to say.

There was only one thing for me to do: leave. As quickly as possible. I somehow got my socks and sneakers on, and wriggled into my t-shirt, wishing I could do it faster. He sat on the bed, still looking down at the sheets.

Without looking back, I walked to the door, unlocked it, and stepped out into the hallway, feeling as if I were fleeing the scene of a crime.

Only when I was back in my car did I feel safe again. The world outside looked as it always did, no changes, no danger. As I started up the engine, I thought again about what I'd just done with Mark and felt another erection coming on.

7. Paper Balls

It really should have been Wendy all along, from the start. I'd wasted my time with the other girls. I really had.

"You like it?" I said.

"Mm."

We were in the living room of Wendy's house and there was no one else home. All the lights were turned out and the television was on without any sound. We were on the sofa and my hands were up under her sweater. Her face looked flushed.

I'd finally decided that a quiet girl like Wendy was the best thing for me. With her, there was no pressure. I felt comfortable being with her. And everyone else seemed to think we were meant for each other. We were one of the school's more prominent couples.

Though in fact we'd only been going steady for a month, most people had the impression that we'd been going together for much longer.

I'd made it clear to her from the start that there was to be no sex until we were more seriously committed. I warned her of the dangers of teenage pregnancy, backing it up with what Jack had experienced. Not even a condom ensured safety. The best thing was abstinence. And I emerged as a gentleman, a responsible and caring boy, unlike most of the others.

But she said kissing was enough for her. Some of her girl-friends who were sexually active had confessed to her that they preferred kissing to sex. It was much more romantic and arousing than the brutal thrusting which only gave them pain or a feeling of being used.

Wendy herself was a virgin and had no intention of using sex as a substitute for tenderness. Not that she wanted to save it till marriage. But her values were traditional. I was happy with that. I suspected she might even be afraid of sex...

If so, that made two of us. Ever since that afternoon in Mark's bedroom, I was afraid I might have been 'branded', that I could never enjoy normal sex with a girl. And I was afraid to find out.

Sometimes I couldn't believe I'd actually done it. The more time passed, the more like a dream it became. It seemed like some dirty fantasy I'd invented in my mind. I knew all the details of that afternoon by heart now... there were times when I couldn't get the scene out of my mind. It played and re-played in my mind like a movie I couldn't take my eyes away from.

Certain moments of that afternoon would return sometimes, often at the most unexpected moments. Even as I was kissing Wendy now, I could feel his body, the ghost of his body, and my kisses became more inflamed.

I pulled away from the kiss.

"Look what you're doing to me." I indicated the hard bulge at my groin.

"What a bad boy you are."

"But it's all your fault," I said. "You're doing this to me."

She giggled. "And everyone thinks you're such a gentleman."

"No boy's a gentleman when he's with his girlfriend. Come on, touch me."

"Well..."

Seeing her hesitate, I took her hand and brought it down onto the hardness.

We played games like this without losing control of ourselves, proud of our maturity. And I was secretly glad it didn't have to go beyond this. I should never have tried to force myself to lose my virginity.

I still couldn't believe that I'd fucked a boy and it had left no mark upon me. I would have expected the whole world to know. This face of mine which everyone looked at—didn't it give me away every time I thought about what I'd done? Eating dinner with my family, talking with my teachers and friends in school as if nothing were different... wasn't I a spy carrying a deadly secret? But on the surface, I looked as I'd always looked. It was only inside where I'd been touched with a magic wand—where I'd stepped into the ring of fire and stepped back out again unscathed, unsinged.

It had been a fluke, a slip. A part of me had always been curious: what would it be like to do it—if not with Mark, then with another boy. A lot of boys wondered.

But it was all behind me now, safely behind. Mark and I could no longer be friends. I hadn't gone back to his house since then. In fact, I was avoiding him at school. But he seemed to be used to it. Maybe all the other boys he mentioned did the same thing, out of guilt or fear of discovery—or perhaps to kill the temptation of wanting a repeat performance.

Maybe it was my imagination, but he seemed hurt by my

neglect, and sometimes made biting remarks about me behind my back. But I didn't worry too much about his telling anyone about what had happened. I knew I could always deny it, and claim it was another one of his lies. After all, there was no proof that it had even happened.

And my high profile with Wendy made any such rumors about me unlikely. People had such a strong image of me as Wendy's steady boyfriend that no one would have believed that I'd done anything with Mark. And the more time I spent with her, the more I felt I could rub out the memory of that afternoon.

If I put that one mistake behind me, it would be as if it had never happened. Unlike Mark, I was just a normal boy with normal desires, no different from any other boy. The straight and narrow path would be much better for me in the long run. After all, I had my whole life ahead of me. It wasn't determined by fifteen minutes in a friend's bedroom.

Yes, no one knew. And no one would ever know.

Wendy giggled again. Smiling wickedly, she whispered, "Shall I give you a hand?"

"I think I'd like that," I said, my voice almost breaking. "I'd like that very much..."

She smilingly reached for my zipper, but froze at the sound of a car coming up the driveway.

"Oh God. It's my brother."

"Your brother? I didn't know he was in town."

"He's home on leave right now. He was out drinking with some friends."

We pulled apart and I reached for the television's remote control and turned up the volume as Wendy straightened herself up.

The front door opened and we both turned to look.

There in the doorway, standing with the careless languor of a powerful jungle animal was a young man in his early twenties. He wore faded blue jeans frayed at the cuffs, and his slender, sockless feet seemed to flow into his clean white tennis shoes. His t-shirt fit him so tightly that his muscular chest seemed to swell it out, expanding and stretching it with each breath he took, threatening to burst his upper torso free of its confinement. A sleeve was rolled up on one side, showing the solid bulging of his upper arm, and tucked into the fold of the sleeve was a crumpled pack of cigarettes. His hair was cut very short, showing to advantage his well-shaped head and finely-formed ears.

Just as he turned his head toward us (a cigarette hanging loosely from the corner of his mouth), I caught a certain look in his eyes, a dreamy, far-off gaze as if he were peering at a distant horizon, his lips pursed pensively, his eyelids half-shut in a seductive droop.

He paused in the doorway to stare at us.

Wendy stirred. "Sean, this is my boyfriend, Guy Willard."

I got to my feet. Sean strolled over to us, his hand already extended in a handshake. I grasped it, surprised and thrilled at the firmness of his grip. I gazed into eyes whose deep azure formed a stunning contrast with his dark, almost black hair.

"Hi," I whispered.

"Hello, Guy. I've heard a lot about you." His grip was powerful.

Dimly, I heard Wendy say, "This is my brother Sean. He's in the Navy."

"Oh?"

I would have guessed as much even without something which caught and rivetted my attention: a sinister-looking tattoo on his upper arm of a deadly, rainbow-hued scorpion.

Noticing my appraisal of it, his brow twitched as though he were repressing a shy grin. With embarrassed pride, he jerked his head down toward it, muttering, "I got that in Hong Kong."

"Wow."

"Listen, I just stopped in for a pack of cigarettes. I'm on my way out now."

"Don't leave on my account," I said.

"I'm not." He got a new pack of cigarettes from the counter and tapped it against the wall, then came over to me and punched my shoulder lightly. "Why should I wanna stick around here on a Saturday night, right?" He winked at me and turned to go.

And as quickly as he'd come over to greet me, he gave a curt nod and left the house, leaving a sudden gaping hole in my universe.

"It was great of your brother to leave us alone."

"Yes. He's really understanding."

We listened to the car start up again and pull out of the driveway.

"In a way I feel bad about it..."

"Don't. He likes nothing better than to go out drinking with his old high school buddies. They were always getting into trouble with their parents and the police. A real rebel."

Even after he was gone, the whole house for me became filled with the essence of Sean. I pictured him riding through the dark like a moody, romantic hero. Nothing could touch the solitary inner core which lay at the heart of his being.

"Is he on a ship?"

"Yeah. But it's in port now in San Diego, and he's on a two-week leave. Come on, I'll show you a picture of his ship."

I followed her upstairs and she opened the door of the room at the far end of the hallway.

"This is his room. What a mess."

"Is it okay to go inside?"

"Of course."

It was a small room, furnished with a cot and a dresser. There was a seabag in the corner and some dirty laundry lying about.

Wendy led me over to the dresser. She opened a drawer and picked out a stack of photographs, then began leafing through them.

"Look. This is his ship."

She handed me one of the photos and I looked at it. It showed a gray ship in a dock somewhere, among a lot of other gray ships. Some sailors were walking around but I couldn't pick out Sean.

She was still flipping through the stack as she handed me another one.

"And this is the kind of thing he does on shore leave."

Sean and some other friends were in civilian clothes, in a bar someplace with a lot of Oriental women. They all looked drunk. Sean was sitting at a counter with his arm around a woman's waist. His eyes looked a little bleary.

"And look at this one. This is a British girl he met in Greece, a student, I think. She was hiking around Europe when she ran into my brother in Athens. She keeps sending him letters. I think he promised to marry her or something. He's terrible."

But another photo in the stack had caught my eye. I pulled it out. "What's this?"

It showed Sean, shirtless, leaning jauntily back against something, a bench or a rope. With his thumbs hooked loosely in his belt-loops, he was squinting in the glare of the sun... or perhaps he was expressing his contempt for the photographer, for his face wore a hint of a sneer, tinged with mockery or even cruelty. It was impossible to tell where the picture had been taken, whether it was on some beach or on the deck of a ship. Behind him was the sea, of a particular shade of blue I had never seen before in my life. It was impossible to pinpoint where sky and sea met. The whole background was blurred into a formless, creamy texture, making Sean's bare torso seem suspended, like an angel's, against a backdrop of azure. The light from the setting sun caused his skin to glow and shimmer eerily.

Physically, Sean was perfect. He had all of Jack's aggressive masculinity, but without the adolescent bravado; he had Mark's androgynous sensuality without the vindictive spite. As I studied the photograph, my insides seemed to reverberate with a mellow tone as though a bell had just been rung, a bell whose achingly beautiful sound announced a message for my ears only.

I felt as if I were gazing into a place where reality intersected with my dreams and fantasies. An exotic feeling of adventure had keened through me as a little boy whenever I dreamed of life on the high seas with an ideal boyhood friend, soaked in the hiss of sea spray and the smell of brine. Sean reminded me of the long-lost ideal partner of my boyhood daydreams. It felt like a reunion...

"That was taken by one of his friends in the Navy." She snatched it lightly from my fingers, and after glancing at it momentarily, replaced it in the stack. "Come on. We've got better things to do than talk about my brother."

"Yeah."

"How about if we go to my bedroom? That way, no one can bother us again."

"All right."

In the privacy of her bedroom, with the door closed, we tried to return to where we'd left off. But it felt too contrived, too mechanical. Something was missing; I was only going through the motions. And she knew it.

She pulled away from the kiss. "How come you're so quiet all of a sudden?" she said.

"I don't know. I guess I just lost my concentration."

"Damn my brother for coming in just then."

"It wasn't his fault," I murmured.

"It was. It was." She looked ready to cry.

"Come on, let's try it again."

I gazed at the closed door and thought of the short distance down the hallway to his room. I thought of the scorpion tattoo. Its tail had been raised, poised to strike, and the tiny sting, by dint of the tattooer's art, had actually appeared to twinkle. Maybe it was the light glinting off a drop of poison on its tip.

*   *   *

It was much later. It was dark. I heard the door open. He came in and turned on the light. When he saw me, he was momentarily startled, but that passed. He didn't seem too surprised to find me there.

"You waited for me?" he said.

"Yeah."

"How did you know I wouldn't mind?"

"I just knew."

Though I was acting so nonchalant, in fact I was ecstatic. I'd been right! Right! He knew!

"Where's Wendy?" he said.

"She's sleeping in her room. That's why we have to be quiet."

"I figured as much." He turned off the room light and went over to the night table and turned on a tiny reading lamp. Its red shade put a strange glow in the room, a glow strangely reminiscent of the light in the photograph I'd seen of him.

"Do you know Mark Warren?" I asked on an impulse.

"Mark Warren? No. Who's he?"

"No one special."

"Listen, I'm gonna change. I hope you don't mind."

"No. Go right ahead."

He tossed the pack of cigarettes onto the bed then began slipping off his t-shirt. As his upper torso came into view, I saw that it was just like his body in the photo. There was even the same glow. And the expression on his face was exactly the same. Only now I understood the meaning of the contempt in his eyes: he knew what it was that I wanted. But I didn't care. I thought of all the times I'd dreamed of something like this. I thought of how easy it all was if you just didn't think about it too much.

I found myself moving toward him, sinking to my knees.

He just stood there as I reached up and undid the snap on his jeans, then pulled the zipper down.

He wasn't wearing any underwear. As I slid the jeans down his thighs, his half-erect penis popped out and bobbed for a moment before my face, then reared up with a series of twitches until it was nuzzled flat against his stomach.

Fully erect, it was exactly the size of my own. The sight made

190

me dizzy. I reached up and felt his hardness, shyly at first, and then grasped it more boldly and stroked it. I looked up to see his reaction.

His eyes went wide as he gazed down at me with just the hint of a smile.

My hand trembled as I held him. I shifted my weight so I could bring my face closer.

Like all boys, I'd often fantasized about being able to suck my own penis. I'd once seen a photo of an Indian yogi who'd bent his body so that his face was down at his groin. If he hadn't been wearing swim trunks, he could easily have sucked himself off. That photo had always haunted me. Try as I might, I could never duplicate the posture.

Now my face was so close to Sean's dick that I could feel the damp heat from it as it quivered and twitched in response to my stroking. I caught a whiff of the familiar spermy smell which all young boys seem to carry about them like a symbol of their youthful malehood. It was a perfume I often caught from a passing boy, or in a friend's bedroom.

Now I could do something about it. Now all my dreams were about to come true.

I hesitated for the briefest moment, to overcome a momentary squeamishness. But my desire was too strong to hold back. As I lowered my face I felt as if I were breaking the tensile surface which separates fantasy from reality. I tracked a slow, careful lick along the entire length of his dick, from the pulsing root all the way up to the moist tip. Holding the hot captive in a tight grip I had another moment of stage fright; I felt all the eyes of the world upon me. Any moment now, the whole world would burst in and catch me in the act. Then, carried away by some fierce and deep momentum, I banished all thought from my mind and set to work.

Though I was doing it for the first time in my life, I found myself taking to it instinctively and naturally, as most boys do, knowing best how to provoke and satisfy their own desires. I closed my lips around the warm flesh and held it in my mouth before doing anything. Except for the slight salt taste, it was everything I'd expected; the throbbing warmth seemed to melt the softness of my mouth like butter.

I filled my mouth with as much as I could without gagging. Then I began to move, bobbing back and forth, my sucking making my lips stretch out. I could feel the ridges and bumps, even the veins.

Still holding his dick tightly with one hand I went to work with my lips and tongue, concentrating on the glans, rolling its smooth roundness around in my lips, making it slick with my spit. I thought of the lollipops I'd licked and sucked as a child—lime green, strawberry red, lemon yellow—all precursors to this hot pink one...as if all the childhood candy was an elaborate preparation for just this moment. I imagined a lollipop thrust deep into my mouth as I twirled its stick, giving it loving caresses of my tongue, worrying and worrying its tantalizing sweet roundness, rolling and curling my tongue over, under, around it.

There was a certain sense of power in knowing the pleasure my mouth was giving him. I kissed the hot head and with the very tip of my tongue worried away at that strip of skin just under the glans which is the most sensitive spot on a boy. Then I twirled my tongue around the circumference of the head in a continuous fluttering.

I was as good as Mark. I was better than Mark.

With my free hand I reached up and touched his balls, crinkled up small and tight now against his groin. As I stroked them, his dick twitched in response. I bent my face down again and clamped my lips tightly around the entire glans, slowly taking in as much as I could. Then I moved my head up and down to stroke it, feeling his fingers raking through my hair, then close tightly against my temples, urging me on. As if from a distance I heard his soft whimpers; it wouldn't be long now before I could experience the sensation I'd dreamed of so often: the warm explosion in my mouth which signalled the wrenching climax of another boy's pleasure.

It felt good. Nothing had ever felt this good. I knew he was poised on the verge of coming because I myself was.

His hands gripped the sides of my head and his pelvis pumped his dick into my mouth hard, two, three, four times. And then he stopped and held still; I felt his whole body tremble as his dick twitched spasmodically and sudden warmth filled my mouth.

And I was coming, too.

* * *

"Oh!"

192

I was coming, awake now, into my pants as I popped my eyes open in the dark.

My heart hammering, and still trying to figure out what had happened, I lay still and felt the uncomfortable clamminess in my briefs, the tacky trickle of warm semen into my pubic bush.

I was in my own room. It had been a wet dream. I looked at the clock and saw it was two o'clock in the morning. The house was dark and quiet.

I lay there for a long while before finally mustering the energy to get up and change out of my soiled underwear. In the dark, I cleaned myself up with some tissues and got out another pair of briefs from the dresser. The new pair felt refreshing.

Silently I crept out into the hallway and deposited the soiled pair in the hamper by the bathroom, then returned to my bed. I still couldn't shake the incredible disappointment of waking up to reality. The dream had been so real that my regret was poignant; I felt all the anguish of an actual forced parting.

I turned on the lamp and reached down between the mattress and bedsprings to pull out the photo. I'd sneaked into Sean's room and stolen it from the bundle of photos in his dresser while Wendy was in the bathroom. From the moment I'd seen it, I knew I'd end up stealing it. After that, it was all I could do to give a convincing performance of reluctantly parting from Wendy...

And coming home tonight, before going to sleep, I'd masturbated twice to the picture. But even that hadn't been enough. My sleeping mind had returned to the image of my desire, to tease me with it, to give me the fuller satisfaction I craved.

I felt now as if I'd eaten the rotten fruit which has fallen off a forbidden tree. But I'd had no compunctions about eating it, knowing that its very sweetness came from its forbiddenness. Why did it have to taste so delicious if it was rotten? Why did our poisons have to be so seductive?

I pulled the photo closer, and then put my lips to Sean's face, his chest, then closed my eyes. If Sean had wanted it, I would have gladly done the same thing in real life. But of course it could never happen.

... Could it?

I thought of Mark, and what we'd done in his bedroom. It had been good. I couldn't deny it. As I remembered all the details of what we'd done, I felt a hard knot settle in my stomach. I suddenly knew I would do it again sometime, if not with Mark, then with someone else very much like him. Another faggot.

I thought of all the faggots in school, of all the faggots in the world.

I remembered that morning long ago when I'd first heard the word. It had sounded so innocuous. In fact, it still did; the dictionary on my desk defined faggot as 'a bundle of sticks or twigs, esp. for use as fuel'. I knew: I'd looked it up so many times.

Some boys go through a phase... which they outgrow in time...those who don't are called... from the Greek word...

I thought of Mark Warren, and how it must feel to be a faggot.

I thought of Jack as he'd looked at his peak, his beautiful peak, and of the sad new Jack.

I thought of Sean.

I thought of Bobby and our little games, our innocent games.

I thought of Mark again, and of how his dick had looked as I was fucking him in the ass.

I thought of Bobby's dick, the first hard-on I'd seen on another boy.

I thought of all the boys in the shower room, moving slowly in a mist of desire.

I thought of Sean again.

I thought of how his dick had looked in my dream.

"Kind of salty... like a warm, salty gob in your mouth."

The hard knot in my stomach wouldn't go away. I felt all weak inside.

I got up from the bed and walked over to my desk and sat down. From the top drawer I pulled out a packet of notebook paper, bought so eagerly in the fall of my first year of high school along with notebooks and color-coded subject dividers. After three years' use, the plastic-wrapped packet of ruled sheets looked shabby and bedraggled, but many fresh, unused sheets still remained at the bottom, perhaps fifty of them.

I slipped one out and laid it flat upon my desk top. I stared at its cool clean whiteness for a long, long time. Then, taking up a pencil, I printed carefully upon it in even block letters, with cruel precision: GUY WILLARD IS A FAGGOT.

I tried to imagine it scrawled upon the boys' room walls where I'd seen so many similar accusations inscribed (with only the name— the many names!—different.) Suddenly I began trembling like a leaf, violently, as if I were in the clutches of a fever, but there was no fever. My teeth were chattering uncontrollably; I closed my eyes. When it finally subsided, I began to feel a satisfying glow of pain gradually welling up inside me.

So that's what it felt like. It wasn't so bad.

I took another look at what I'd written, then crumpled it up and threw it away. I drew out another sheet and wrote upon it again: GUY WILLARD IS A FAGGOT.

I stared at it for a long, long time, then crumpled it up, too.

As if pressed onward by urgent warnings, I wrote the same message on all the remaining sheets, until I had no more left, until the floor around my desk was littered with piles of crumpled-up paper balls.

Ulster Alien *by Stephen Birkett*
A poignant coming-out story set amidst the troubles of Northern Ireland.

Meet Matthew Woodhead - a sensitive child with his beloved best-friend Danny; an awkward teenager struggling to fit in with the gang; a young gay man on the brink of coming out. But in Northern Ireland everything is more complicated. Matthew's journey to adulthood takes place against a background of civil rights protests, terrorist bombings and the Save Ulster From Sodomy campaign. A world where young lives are destroyed by murder, and young minds by sectarian bigotry. Closely modelled on his own experience, Stephen Birkett portrays a world where the bonds of male friendship are strong, but a gay identity is that much harder to attain.

price - £9.95

ISBN : 1 902852 01 X

Teleny *by Oscar Wilde*
The only complete edition of this erotic tale

First published in 1893, this outrageous novel of homosexual love has been attributed to Oscar Wilde with varying degrees of certainty. This edition, carefully prepared from original sources in the British Library archives, is the only one on sale annotated and unabridged. Ahead of its time in its celebration of uninhibited sensual passion between men.

"It is a bizarre book, alternating porn with florid purple passages, a hymn to sodomy with an angry attack on notions of the 'natural'" New Statesman.

price - £9.95

ISBN : 1 902852 00 1

All the Queen's Men *by Nick Elwood*

A revealing account of fourteen years as an openly gay man in the British Army.

"Out for most of my career as a cavalry bandsman, I discovered a gay military world where many squaddies were partial to a bit of cock fun. I indulged in numerous flirtations and affairs. There were no threats and rarely any hostility. Encounters with the Military Police, at first invasive grew into an irrepressible reckless defiance. We banded together, protected by peers and senior ranks alike.

I became engaged to a 16-year-old civilian, lithe and brown eyed Andreas, the summer soulmate of my dreams. Working up through the ranks to Trumpet Major I experienced much during my army career, pride in my sexuality, elation and loss. What a bummer it is to be in love."

price - £9.95

ISBN : 1 902852 03 6

Banged Up *by Jack Dickson*

Detective Jas Anderson, the hero of "Freeform" is imprisoned and fighting for his life in this new adventure.

Detective-Sergeant Jas Anderson, the violent anti-hero of Freeform, ended that story being expelled from the Glasgow police force. Banged Up starts with Jas being framed by his ex-colleagues, and remanded to Barlinnie prison. Soon he is forced to share a cell with Steve McStay, sentenced for Aggravated Assault on two gay men. In this all-male enviroment, inmates don't divide into gay and staight, rather into who fucks and who gets fucked. But resilient as ever, Jas forms an unlikely partnership with Steve in his fight survival.

price - £9.95

ISBN : 1 902852 04 4

Growing Pains *by Mike Seabrook*

The sequel to this author's most popular novel "out of bounds".

Mike Seabrook's many fans will remember Stephen Hill, the dashing young cricketer from Out of Bounds, his teacher and lover Graham, and his clever schoolfriend Richard. Two years after Stephen was forced to leave home, Graham dies in a plane crash, and Steven comes into an unexpected legacy, including a large country pub in Sussex. But as well as the strains this new fortune places on his relationship with friend Richard, the pair have to confront the homophobia of a group of the villagers, resentful of the changes Steven and Richard bring into their lives. Things finally come to a head when a young boy is brutally raped and left for dead.

price - £9.95

ISBN : 1 902852 05 2

The above books can be ordered through the outlet where this volume was purchased or direct from the publisher (enclose £1.95 p&p in the UK or £5 overseas) :

GMP Mail Order, 3 Broadbent Close London N6 5GG.

Cheques payable to 'MaleXpress Ltd.'

(or call 0800 45 45 66 for our catalogue)